HELP® ELEMENTARY

Handbook of Exercises for Language Processing

Andrea M. Lazzari
Patricia M. Peters

D1478082

T4-ALF-967

Skill Area:	Language
Ages:	6 – 12

LinguiSystems

LinguiSystems, Inc.
3100 4th Avenue
East Moline, IL 61244

1-800-PRO IDEA
1-800-776-4332

Printed in the U.S.A.
ISBN 1-55999-259-X

About the Authors

Andrea M. Lazzari

Andrea M. Lazzari, Ed. D., is an assistant professor of special education at Virginia Commonwealth University in Richmond, Virginia. She has worked as a speech-language pathologist in the public schools, in a community clinic, and in private practice. She has also been a teacher of preschool handicapped students and the Supervisor of Early Childhood Special Education Programs for the state of Virginia. *HELP Elementary* is Andrea's eleventh publication with LinguiSystems. She is also the author of *Just for Adults* and co-author of *HELP 1, HELP 2, HELP 3, HELP 4, HELP 1 & 2 Language Pictures, HELP 3 & 4 Language Pictures, HELP 1 & 2 Language Game, HELP 3 & 4 Language Game,* and *HELP 5.*

Patricia M. Peters

Patricia M. Peters, M. Ed., CCC is employed as a speech-language pathologist by Rehabilitation Services of Roanoke, Inc., Roanoke, Virginia. She works with a communicatively disordered population ranging from preschool through geriatric ages. *HELP Elementary* is Patricia's tenth publication with LinguiSystems. She is also the co-author of *HELP 1, HELP 2, HELP 3, HELP 4, HELP 1 & 2 Language Pictures, HELP 3 & 4 Language Pictures, HELP 1 & 2 Language Game, HELP 3 & 4 Language Game,* and *HELP 5.*

April 1993

Dedication

To our children, Sarah and Brian
And Tamara
For the joy they've brought to our lives
And to our young clients who have touched our lives and
dared us to imagine

HELP Elementary was developed for you by Jennell Bergwall, Kathy Black, Beth Ducey, Kelly Fischer, Lynette Johnson, Candy McMahon, Janet Meyers, Sharon VanDaele, and Barb Walter.

Illustrations were done by Paul Lange.

Table of Contents

Introduction

Since the introduction of the *HELP* series in 1980 with the publication of *HELP 1* and *HELP 2*, ongoing efforts have been made to respond to the ever-changing needs of our consumers and their efforts to address the language needs of their clients. Some formatting changes, such as moving answers to the back of the book and using a spiral-bound cover to make photocopying easier, dramatically changed the way in which the *HELP* volumes could be used. Throughout these requested changes, as well as other revisions over the years, the original attention to detail, the gradual increase of complexity within and between sections, and the comprehensive nature of the *HELP* series have been maintained in each volume. This new addition to the series, *HELP Elementary*, reflects our continuing responsiveness to meeting the needs of clinicians, teachers, and paraprofessionals . . . a *HELP* book just for kids.

HELP Elementary combines the best parts of the previous *HELP 1-5* volumes, using new stimulus items within familiar, trusted lessons. The difficulty level of this material ranges from grades first through sixth and includes the most requested and appropriate lessons from ten units in the original five *HELP* volumes. New items have been generated to provide more stimulus items specific to the elementary school-age student. Although the basic format is the same, some lessons were changed slightly to include topics presented in the original *HELP* volumes in a fresh, new manner. Also, slight visual changes were made to the physical appearance of the individual lessons and units to provide an "elementary feel" to the book.

As in previous *HELP* books, *HELP Elementary* takes a no-frills approach to language development and remediation. In presenting as many items as possible with minimal explanation in each lesson, the basis of an effective treatment program is offered that *can* and *should* be expanded and enhanced by the clinician. In doing so, the clinician can ensure that each student's program is individualized to meet his or her needs, while reflecting his or her unique strengths and experiences.

The following guidelines are offered for effective use of the lessons in *HELP Elementary*:

1. Many lessons are presented as written worksheets for the student. Use your own judgment in presenting the lessons orally or as worksheets, depending on the ability of your student and the overall purpose for specific remediation. Even if your goal for a student focuses on written language, it is recommended that each set of exercises be presented orally first, to make sure the student understands the purpose of the lesson and the response format.

2. As the ages and skills of the students will vary, use your own judgment to decide which portions of each section to use with individual students. Items within each lesson have been sequenced, when possible, from the easier items to the more difficult. The same arrangement is true for lessons within a single unit.

3. Common, correct responses have been provided for almost all items in the answer key. There may be other acceptable answers, depending on the student's experiences and cultural background. Again, use your discretion in determining correctness of response.

4. Many repetitions of items may be necessary before target accuracy levels are reached. Keep track of performance on the specific items chosen to be within the student's ability range.

5. Strive to achieve carryover of target areas in conversation in everyday and classroom activities through constant repetition, questioning, and stressing of specific concepts. These exercises may also be successfully used by parents and paraprofessionals with some guidance from the clinician. Communication between home and school (or clinic) is essential if carryover is to be effective. Carryover is essential to derive maximum benefit from the *HELP* approach.

Thirteen years after the first *HELP* books became a reality, we proudly offer *HELP Elementary* to our colleagues as the newest member of the *HELP* series. We thank our many colleagues, friends, and family members, as well as the LinguiSystems' staff, for their continued support, suggestions, and encouragement. We hope you will find *HELP Elementary* to be a worthy addition to the *HELP* tradition of comprehensive, practical, and functional language exercises for individuals with communication impairments.

AML
PMP

Question Comprehension

To comprehend language, children must process and understand verbal information provided through the auditory and/or visual channels. Children's understanding of language concepts and their ability to gain meaning from verbal material is essential to their use of these concepts in oral or written expression. Question comprehension takes on added importance in the classroom, where much of instruction and learning takes place in a question and answer format.

In this section, students are cued with a response pattern such as *yes/no, true/false,* or *always/sometimes/never.* This format allows language expansion to take place without being impeded by deficits in verbal expression. As the student progresses, these response cues can be faded. Carryover to the classroom can be fostered by targeting the same format of question and response in oral classroom activities.

Lesson 1

Circle *yes* or *no* to answer each question. The first one is done for you.

1. Can you tear a piece of paper?   (yes)   no

2. Can you ride in a bathtub?   yes   no

3. Can you wear a jacket?   yes   no

4. Can you listen to music?   yes   no

5. Can you swim in a mud puddle?   yes   no

6. Can you walk across the floor?   yes   no

7. Can a marble roll?   yes   no

8. Can you slide up a slide?   yes   no

9. Can you roll a chair?   yes   no

10. Can you pour a piece of bread?   yes   no

11. Can you toast a marshmallow?   yes   no

12. Can you hear the sun?   yes   no

13. Can you open an envelope?   yes   no

14. Can you peel a banana?   yes   no

15. Can you wear a shoe on your head?   yes   no

16. Can milk be sour?   yes   no

17. Can you blow up a balloon?   yes   no

18. Can you stretch a board?   yes   no

19. Can you sing a milk shake?   yes   no

20. Can you drink a cloud?   yes   no

I.E.P. Goal: The student will answer "can" questions with 90% or greater accuracy.

Question Comprehension   8

Name _____

Circle *yes* or *no* to answer each question.

21.	Can you squeeze an orange?	yes	no
22.	Can you unwrap an ocean?	yes	no
23.	Can you hide in a coffee cup?	yes	no
24.	Can you teach a bird to write?	yes	no
25.	Can you fold your hands?	yes	no
26.	Can you use sandpaper to make wood smooth?	yes	no
27.	Can an elephant have a baby rhinoceros?	yes	no
28.	Can you make a coat out of nails?	yes	no
29.	Can you undo a buckle?	yes	no
30.	Can a bubble burst?	yes	no
31.	Can you hop without your foot touching the ground?	yes	no
32.	Can a robber be arrested?	yes	no
33.	Can you outrun a train?	yes	no
34.	Can you melt a crayon in the freezer?	yes	no
35.	Can you go sailing in a bus?	yes	no
36.	Can you buy clothing with cash?	yes	no
37.	Can you make toast without heating the bread?	yes	no
38.	Can you go to sleep without closing your eyes?	yes	no
39.	Can you paint with a sponge?	yes	no
40.	Can an organ be played?	yes	no

I.E.P. Goal: The student will answer "can" questions with 90% or greater accuracy.

Question Comprehension

Circle *yes* or *no* to answer each question.

41.	Can a yo-yo spin?	yes	no
42.	Can a button get wrinkled?	yes	no
43.	Can a gift be shared?	yes	no
44.	Can a clock be slow?	yes	no
45.	Can you row a hammock?	yes	no
46.	Can a sweater unravel?	yes	no
47.	Can a square have only three sides?	yes	no
48.	Can you get sunburned at night?	yes	no
49.	Can you tell time with a yardstick?	yes	no
50.	Can you play a piano without making noise?	yes	no
51.	Can yarn be wound?	yes	no
52.	Can you dive in a pool feet first?	yes	no
53.	Can you play a trumpet without blowing?	yes	no
54.	Can you milk a rooster?	yes	no
55.	Can you pedal a bike without bending your knees?	yes	no
56.	Can you inflate a balloon?	yes	no
57.	Can a stream be chopped down?	yes	no
58.	Can a program be broadcast?	yes	no
59.	Can a race car idle?	yes	no
60.	Can a satellite orbit?	yes	no

I.E.P. Goal: The student will answer "can" questions with 90% or greater accuracy.

Name _____

Circle *yes* or *no* to answer each question.   The first one is done for you.

1. Does a baby wear diapers?   (yes)   no

2. Does a raincoat get wet?   yes   no

3. Does a clown make us laugh?   yes   no

4. Does a police officer wear a badge?   yes   no

5. Does a ball break if you drop it?   yes   no

6. Does a tricycle have four wheels?   yes   no

7. Does a drugstore sell meat?   yes   no

8. Does a grocery store sell fruit?   yes   no

9. Do you wear a bracelet on your neck?   yes   no

10. Does milk come from geese?   yes   no

11. Does a chicken lay quarters?   yes   no

12. Do you have a thumb on your toe?   yes   no

13. Does a rotten banana taste good?   yes   no

14. Does a balloon pop if you stick a pin in it?   yes   no

15. Does a sweater keep you cool in the summer?   yes   no

16. Does a quilt keep you warm?   yes   no

17. Does a shark live in the ocean?   yes   no

18. Does salt make our food taste sweet?   yes   no

19. Does a rocking chair go back and forth?   yes   no

20. Do you wash tissues and use them again?   yes   no

I.E.P. Goal: The student will answer "do/does" questions with 90% or greater accuracy.

Question Comprehension   11

Circle *yes* or *no* to answer each question.

21. Does a light bulb get hot?   yes   no

22. Do bicycles come in different sizes?   yes   no

23. Do trees need water to grow?   yes   no

24. Do dogs sleep standing up?   yes   no

25. Do wild animals wear collars?   yes   no

26. Do shoes come in threes?   yes   no

27. Does an alligator live in a cave?   yes   no

28. Does a peach have fuzz on it?   yes   no

29. Do cats dive in the water?   yes   no

30. Does a bandage help a broken leg get better?   yes   no

31. Does a bus carry passengers?   yes   no

32. Does popcorn come from pumpkin seeds?   yes   no

33. Do mittens have a space for each finger?   yes   no

34. Does a barber use scissors?   yes   no

35. Does December come at the end of the year?   yes   no

36. Does your dentist want you to brush your teeth regularly?   yes   no

37. Do your parents want you to eat healthy foods?   yes   no

38. Does a locked door blow open?   yes   no

39. Does a cut apple turn brown?   yes   no

40. Do monkeys have antlers?   yes   no

I.E.P. Goal: The student will answer "do/does" questions with 90% or greater accuracy.

Name _____

Circle *yes* or *no* to answer each question.

41. Do you grow an inch every day?	yes	no
42. Do you throw away a broom after you use it?	yes	no
43. Do you get fuel from a gas pump?	yes	no
44. Does "Z" come in the middle of the alphabet?	yes	no
45. Does a conductor lead an orchestra?	yes	no
46. Do you exhale to blow a whistle?	yes	no
47. Does boiling water bubble?	yes	no
48. Does a coal miner work underground?	yes	no
49. Does a telephone operator fix telephones?	yes	no
50. Do belt loops hold up your pants?	yes	no
51. Do you use a calculator to add and subtract?	yes	no
52. Does a robin hatch from a sparrow's egg?	yes	no
53. Does a basketball net have a handle on it?	yes	no
54. Do four quarters make a dollar?	yes	no
55. Do ten eggs make a dozen?	yes	no
56. Do two halves make a whole?	yes	no
57. Do you see blossoms on trees in the fall?	yes	no
58. Do your eyelashes grow as fast as your hair?	yes	no
59. Do pretzels have sugar on them?	yes	no
60. Do stopwatches measure seconds?	yes	no

I.E.P. Goal: The student will answer "do/does" questions with 90% or greater accuracy.

Question Comprehension   13

Lesson 3

Name _____

Circle *yes* or *no* to answer each question.   The first one is done for you.

1. If you were a dog, could you bark?   (yes)   no

2. If it is raining outside, is the ground wet?   yes   no

3. If you fold a scarf in half, will it break?   yes   no

4. If you run faster than anyone else, will you win the race?   yes   no

5. If your name is Peter Pan, can you fly?   yes   no

6. If you want to see a tall building, should you go to the city?   yes   no

7. If you were a knife, would you be sharp?   yes   no

8. If you want to buy some shoes, should you go to the doughnut store?   yes   no

9. If you want to see a cow, should you go to the country?   yes   no

10. If you want the baby to nap, should you play loud music in his room?   yes   no

11. If your name is Donald Duck, are you in a cartoon?   yes   no

12. If you have a cat, are you a pet owner?   yes   no

13. If you want to play softball, do you need five bases?   yes   no

14. If you want to make a cake, do you need an oven?   yes   no

15. If you have a needle, but no thread, could you sew on a button?   yes   no

16. If you're wearing boots, should you go swimming with them on?   yes   no

17. If you want to wash your clothes, do you need detergent?   yes   no

18. If you get a splinter in your finger, should you leave it in there?   yes   no

19. If you have a dime, do you have any money?   yes   no

20. If you are in the second grade, are you a teenager?   yes   no

I.E.P. Goal: The student will answer "if" questions with 90% or greater accuracy.

Question Comprehension   14

Name _____

Circle *yes* or *no* to answer each question.

21.	If you were three years old, would you be a grandmother?	yes	no
22.	If you are ten years old, are you an adult?	yes	no
23.	If you go outside at lunchtime, will you need a flashlight?	yes	no
24.	If you have a toothache, should you eat a piece of candy?	yes	no
25.	If you want to do well on a test, should you study hard?	yes	no
26.	If you were a traffic light, would you be red, white, and blue?	yes	no
27.	If you want to surprise someone, should you tell him what you are planning?	yes	no
28.	If you were a canary, could you sing?	yes	no
29.	If you were a construction worker, could you build houses?	yes	no
30.	If you were a bicycle, would you have a chain?	yes	no
31.	If you were a radio, would you have a volume control knob?	yes	no
32.	If you borrow money from someone, should you pay all of it back?	yes	no
33.	If you have two brothers, are you an only child?	yes	no
34.	If your driver stops the school bus at a railroad crossing, should you be quiet?	yes	no
35.	If your mother has two sisters, do you have an aunt?	yes	no
36.	If you pay for a 75-cent item with a dollar bill, should you get change?	yes	no
37.	If your birthday is on Valentine's Day, were you born in February?	yes	no
38.	If today is Friday, is this the middle of the week?	yes	no
39.	If this month is April, is it summertime?	yes	no
40.	If you want to go deep sea diving, do you need oxygen tanks?	yes	no

I.E.P. Goal: The student will answer "if" questions with 90% or greater accuracy.

Question Comprehension   15

Lesson 4

Name _____

Circle *yes* or *no* to answer each question.   The first one is done for you.

1. Do pigs bark?	yes	(no)	21. Do fingernails break?	yes	no
2. Does a telephone ring?	yes	no	22. Do motorcycles wink?	yes	no
3. Do grown-ups sleep?	yes	no	23. Do tables crumble?	yes	no
4. Does an egg bounce?	yes	no	24. Do bulldozers drip?	yes	no
5. Do shirts talk?	yes	no	25. Do nets slice?	yes	no
6. Does a bus stop?	yes	no	26. Does a rainbow clap?	yes	no
7. Does a dog's tail wag?	yes	no	27. Does an umbrella nap?	yes	no
8. Do hearts beat?	yes	no	28. Does paint drip?	yes	no
9. Does a nose hear?	yes	no	29. Do roosters crow?	yes	no
10. Do cats stretch?	yes	no	30. Do doors slam?	yes	no
11. Does a chair cook?	yes	no	31. Does bacon sizzle?	yes	no
12. Do socks rest?	yes	no	32. Does a firecracker pop?	yes	no
13. Does a bowl crack?	yes	no	33. Does a truck wave?	yes	no
14. Does a backpack sweep?	yes	no	34. Does a flag flutter?	yes	no
15. Does a bee gallop?	yes	no	35. Does a wheel spin?	yes	no
16. Does a candle tick?	yes	no	36. Do cars crash?	yes	no
17. Do peanuts lift?	yes	no	37. Does a friend help?	yes	no
18. Does a porch yawn?	yes	no	38. Does a groundhog whistle?	yes	no
19. Do choirs sing?	yes	no	39. Does a traffic light change?	yes	no
20. Do muscles ache?	yes	no	40. Do people dream?	yes	no

I.E.P. Goal: The student will answer "do/does" questions with a noun-verb format with 90% or greater accuracy.

Question Comprehension   16

Name _____

Circle *yes* or *no* to answer each question.

41. Does a ruler measure?	yes no	61. Does a wallet soar?	yes no
42. Does a thumb bend?	yes no	62. Does a scale carve?	yes no
43. Does a zipper shout?	yes no	63. Does a pillow skid?	yes no
44. Does a needle stick?	yes no	64. Do bears hibernate?	yes no
45. Does a bird cough?	yes no	65. Do raincoats protect?	yes no
46. Does a handle turn?	yes no	66. Do fires spread?	yes no
47. Do crackers twist?	yes no	67. Do horns blossom?	yes no
48. Does a nurse care?	yes no	68. Do actors pretend?	yes no
49. Does a hair dryer blow?	yes no	69. Does a sandwich rewind?	yes no
50. Does a parrot talk?	yes no	70. Do shoelaces promise?	yes no
51. Does a parachute open?	yes no	71. Does a cushion stab?	yes no
52. Does a tadpole climb?	yes no	72. Does a chair sigh?	yes no
53. Does a pen leak?	yes no	73. Does a mail carrier deliver?	yes no
54. Does a balloon sweep?	yes no	74. Does a chimpanzee neigh?	yes no
55. Do peaches buzz?	yes no	75. Do students graduate?	yes no
56. Does celery crunch?	yes no	76. Does medicine cure?	yes no
57. Do brakes stop?	yes no	77. Does a puzzle ooze?	yes no
58. Does a teeter-totter kick?	yes no	78. Does a magnet float?	yes no
59. Does a ruler wilt?	yes no	79. Does a leader guide?	yes no
60. Does a baby sob?	yes no	80. Does a newspaper advertise?	yes no

I.E.P. Goal: The student will answer "do/does" questions with a noun-verb format with 90% or greater accuracy.

Question Comprehension   17

Name _____

Circle *yes* or *no* to answer each question.   The first one is done for you.

1. Do all girls have long hair?   yes   (no)

2. Can cats climb trees?   yes   no

3. Can you erase something written in pencil?   yes   no

4. Is two more than ten?   yes   no

5. If you put a log on a fire, will it burn?   yes   no

6. Do wasps sting?   yes   no

7. Can you jump rope with a broken leg?   yes   no

8. Can a baby take a phone message?   yes   no

9. Are a hammer and a saw both tools?   yes   no

10. Can you go to school before you wake up?   yes   no

11. Do all children like physical education class?   yes   no

12. Do some parents help out at school?   yes   no

13. Can you walk under a slide?   yes   no

14. Is a principal the leader of the school?   yes   no

15. Is your foot bigger than your hand?   yes   no

16. Could you make a milk shake without milk?   yes   no

17. Do desks have motors?   yes   no

18. Are green and violet two colors in a rainbow?   yes   no

19. If you were a piano, would you have white and blue keys? yes   no

20. Can a bathtub be mowed?   yes   no

I.E.P. Goal: The student will answer a variety of "yes/no" questions with 90% or greater accuracy.

Name _____

Circle *yes* or *no* to answer each question.

21.	Do cushions become angry?	yes	no
22.	If you were a robot, would you have a heart?	yes	no
23.	Can you play a drum louder than a kazoo?	yes	no
24.	Is relish something used to fix our hair?	yes	no
25.	Is wood stronger than steel?	yes	no
26.	Do fish lick?	yes	no
27.	Does a bed sleep?	yes	no
28.	If you were an orange, would you have sections?	yes	no
29.	Do seals have wings?	yes	no
30.	Is wax an ingredient for brownies?	yes	no
31.	Do helmets protect?	yes	no
32.	Can a switch be flipped?	yes	no
33.	Are single beds wider than double beds?	yes	no
34.	Are pepper and cinnamon spices?	yes	no
35.	Do dentists operate on hearts?	yes	no
36.	Do children grow up to be infants?	yes	no
37.	Can scissors trim?	yes	no
38.	If you were a bicycle, would you have spokes?	yes	no
39.	Do all trees have roots?	yes	no
40.	If you were a spatula, would you have thorns?	yes	no

I.E.P. Goal: The student will answer a variety of "yes/no" questions with 90% or greater accuracy.

Question Comprehension

Lesson 6

Name _____

Circle *some* or *all* to make each statement correct.   The first one is done for you.

1. (Some, (All)) boys have ears.

2. (Some, All) dogs are pets.

3. (Some, All) kittens have stripes.

4. (Some, All) piggy banks are full of money.

5. (Some, All) girls have curly hair.

6. (Some, All) ducks have beaks.

7. (Some, All) cars have tires.

8. (Some, All) children ride the bus to school.

9. (Some, All) ketchup is red.

10. (Some, All) slides are slippery.

11. (Some, All) fish can swim.

12. (Some, All) children have brothers.

13. (Some, All) cups are made of plastic.

14. (Some, All) roses are flowers.

15. (Some, All) balloons are round.

16. (Some, All) cars have four doors.

17. (Some, All) kangaroos can hop.

18. (Some, All) children can jump rope.

19. (Some, All) children go to school.

20. (Some, All) fires are hot.

21. (Some, All) mountains are high.

22. (Some, All) fathers wear glasses.

23. (Some, All) people live in houses.

24. (Some, All) sisters are girls.

25. (Some, All) apples are green.

26. (Some, All) fathers are men.

27. (Some, All) of the time we can see the moon shining.

28. (Some, All) lost pets are found.

29. (Some, All) bathtubs have drains.

30. (Some, All) men drive cars.

31. (Some, All) eggs have shells.

32. (Some, All) boots have laces.

33. (Some, All) bottles are plastic.

34. (Some, All) hotels have rooms.

35. (Some, All) newspapers are recycled.

36. (Some, All) schools have teachers.

37. (Some, All) elevators go up and down.

38. (Some, All) children are good at sports.

39. (Some, All) french fries are crisp.

40. (Some, All) parades are long.

I.E.P. Goal: The student will answer "some/all" questions with 90% or greater accuracy.

Question Comprehension   20

Name _____

Circle *some* or *all* to make each statement correct.

41. (Some, All) jokes are funny.

42. (Some, All) basketball players are short.

43. (Some, All) actors appear in movies.

44. (Some, All) people live to be 75 years old.

45. (Some, All) trees live for 100 years.

46. (Some, All) grandfathers are bald.

47. (Some, All) toothbrushes have bristles.

48. (Some, All) squares have four sides.

49. (Some, All) hats have brims.

50. (Some, All) televisions show programs in color.

51. (Some, All) shoes have soles.

52. (Some, All) blankets are made of wool.

53. (Some, All) seeds will sprout.

54. (Some, All) people have lungs.

55. (Some, All) dentists are men.

56. (Some, All) oceans are deep.

57. (Some, All) musicians can play the piano.

58. (Some, All) T-shirts have writing on them.

59. (Some, All) fans spin around.

60. (Some, All) scissors have handles.

61. (Some, All) radios are portable.

62. (Some, All) people have last names.

63. (Some, All) food can be eaten raw.

64. (Some, All) globes are round.

65. (Some, All) sentences have periods at the end.

66. (Some, All) states have capitals.

67. (Some, All) dreams come true.

68. (Some, All) chains have links.

69. (Some, All) words have at least one vowel.

70. (Some, All) students will graduate from high school.

71. (Some, All) criminals pay for their crimes.

72. (Some, All) books have tables of contents.

73. (Some, All) clocks have second hands.

74. (Some, All) months are 30 days long.

75. (Some, All) glasses have lenses.

76. (Some, All) ladders have rungs.

77. (Some, All) numbers can be divided by one.

78. (Some, All) locks have keys.

79. (Some, All) trios have three members.

80. (Some, All) stories have plots.

I.E.P. Goal: The student will answer "some/all" questions with 90% or greater accuracy.

Question Comprehension

21

 **Lesson 7**

Name _____

Read the statements below and decide if each one is true or false.   Then, circle *true* or *false* for your answer.   The first one is done for you.

1. Betty is a girl's name.   (true)   false

2. A car can go as fast as a train.   true   false

3. Soup is a hot food.   true   false

4. Wallets are used to hold cold drinks.   true   false

5. Nurses fix broken cars.   true   false

6. Goats sleep in trees.   true   false

7. Babies are born without teeth.   true   false

8. You can rest your head on a pillow.   true   false

9. Dry leaves burn easily.   true   false

10. Horses eat fried chicken for dinner.   true   false

11. Frosting is spread on top of cakes.   true   false

12. Windshield wipers help you cut the grass.   true   false

13. Carrots are a juicy fruit.   true   false

14. Snails are bigger than ants.   true   false

15. A baby horse is called a calf.   true   false

16. Apples are sweeter than lemons.   true   false

17. Lettuce is a leafy vegetable.   true   false

18. Carrots grow on bushes.   true   false

19. If you cut your toenails, they won't grow back.   true   false

20. We keep money in a safe.   true   false

I.E.P. Goal: The student will answer "true/false" questions with 90% or greater accuracy.

Question Comprehension   22

Name _____

Read the statements below and decide if each one is true or false.   Then, circle *true* or *false* for your answer.

21. Crabs live in the ocean.   true   false

22. A pair of scissors is used to open cans.   true   false

23. Baby kittens are hatched from eggs.   true   false

24. On Monday morning, all children go to the park.   true   false

25. Teenagers go to high school.   true   false

26. Binoculars help us see things that are far away.   true   false

27. Basketball is played on a field.   true   false

28. Pilots drive trains.   true   false

29. Sweaters are made from bark.   true   false

30. A minute is longer than a second.   true   false

31. A petunia is a kind of bird.   true   false

32. A microphone makes your voice louder.   true   false

33. Summer is the season after winter.   true   false

34. Corduroy is a type of cloth.   true   false

35. A comedian tells jokes.   true   false

36. A dozen is more than a pair.   true   false

37. Rectangles have curved sides.   true   false

38. September has 30 days.   true   false

39. There are only 300 days in a year.   true   false

40. You can use the same calendar every year.   true   false

I.E.P. Goal: The student will answer "true/false" questions with 90% or greater accuracy.

Question Comprehension   23

Name _____

Read the statements below and decide how often each one is true.   Then, circle *always*, *sometimes*, or *never* for your answer.   The first one is done for you.

1. A cat has paws.	(always)	sometimes	never
2. A television rings.	always	sometimes	never
3. A cow barks.	always	sometimes	never
4. A bed is soft.	always	sometimes	never
5. A pencil is sharp.	always	sometimes	never
6. Uncles are men.	always	sometimes	never
7. It rains in the winter.	always	sometimes	never
8. Peas are green vegetables.	always	sometimes	never
9. A button is round.	always	sometimes	never
10. Babies cry when they're sleepy.	always	sometimes	never
11. A singer has a sore throat.	always	sometimes	never
12. Wednesday is after Tuesday.	always	sometimes	never
13. December is in the summer.	always	sometimes	never
14. Footballs are round.	always	sometimes	never
15. Girls wear dresses.	always	sometimes	never
16. Socks have zippers in them.	always	sometimes	never
17. Soup has noodles in it.	always	sometimes	never
18. Men have short hair.	always	sometimes	never
19. Pens run out of ink.	always	sometimes	never
20. Sugar is sweet.	always	sometimes	never

I.E.P. Goal: The student will tell if statements are always, sometimes, or never true with 90% or greater accuracy.

Question Comprehension

Read the statements below and decide how often each one is true.   Then, circle *always*, *sometimes*, or *never* for your answer.

21. Pajamas have long sleeves.	always	sometimes	never
22. A motorcycle has four wheels.	always	sometimes	never
23. Eleven follows ten.	always	sometimes	never
24. Sheep have puppies.	always	sometimes	never
25. "Book" rhymes with "cook."	always	sometimes	never
26. Fifty cents is more than a dollar.	always	sometimes	never
27. Children go to school on Monday.	always	sometimes	never
28. Pizza has cheese on it.	always	sometimes	never
29. A spoon has bristles.	always	sometimes	never
30. Spelling involves letters.	always	sometimes	never
31. Fog is clear.	always	sometimes	never
32. A telephone book has names listed in alphabetical order.	always	sometimes	never
33. Oranges are oval in shape.	always	sometimes	never
34. Police officers wear uniforms.	always	sometimes	never
35. A traffic light turns purple.	always	sometimes	never
36. An oven is hot.	always	sometimes	never
37. Gasoline is a good beverage.	always	sometimes	never
38. Schools are open in the summer.	always	sometimes	never
39. Apples have cores.	always	sometimes	never
40. Bread is made from peas.	always	sometimes	never

I.E.P. Goal: The student will tell if statements are always, sometimes, or never true with 90% or greater accuracy.

Name _____

Read the statements below and decide how often each one is true. Then, circle *always*, *sometimes*, or *never* for your answer.

41. Twins look exactly alike.	always	sometimes	never
42. Baseball bats are made of leather.	always	sometimes	never
43. You should talk to strangers when you are alone.	always	sometimes	never
44. Cabbage is purple.	always	sometimes	never
45. Dollar bills are shaped like rectangles.	always	sometimes	never
46. Football fields are shaped like triangles.	always	sometimes	never
47. Sunglasses have tinted lenses.	always	sometimes	never
48. A firefly becomes a butterfly.	always	sometimes	never
49. A snake sheds its skin.	always	sometimes	never
50. Fire fighters check their equipment after fires.	always	sometimes	never
51. Raisins come from grapes.	always	sometimes	never
52. You can see your shadow.	always	sometimes	never
53. The shell of an egg is fragile.	always	sometimes	never
54. Turkeys fly south for the winter.	always	sometimes	never
55. Seven is an odd number.	always	sometimes	never
56. A zipper has teeth.	always	sometimes	never
57. Ice boils.	always	sometimes	never
58. Butter is made from cream.	always	sometimes	never
59. The earth is in the solar system.	always	sometimes	never
60. A magnet sticks to wood.	always	sometimes	never

I.E.P. Goal: The student will tell if statements are always, sometimes, or never true with 90% or greater accuracy.

Association

Association is the process of attaching meaning to stimuli after it has been received by the auditory or visual channel – the synthesizing of material that has been received. It interconnects receptive language concepts, assimilating experiences for future expression.

Students with language deficits may have particular difficulty associating new stimuli with previous experiences or may not see the commonalities between words, statements, and events without cues. For this reason, it may be necessary to supply many visual cues to aid in the formation of verbal associations. These cues, such as the formation of the initial phoneme of the desired response or actually pointing to the object which represents the correct response, should be faded gradually until the student can make an association solely on the basis of the auditory or visual stimuli.

Development of association skills should be carried out in an environmental context. Questioning the student about daily activities both in and out of the classroom, and relating these activities to past or future experiences can help the student form associations in the real world. In doing so, the student can learn to associate information across academic subjects and in response to different people, events, and situations.

 **Lesson 1**

Name _____

Finish each sentence.   The first one is done for you.

1. If you are hungry, then *eat something*   .

2. If your hands are dirty, then _____.

3. If the telephone rings, then _____.

4. If your socks get wet, then _____.

5. If the toast burns, then _____.

6. If the school bell rings, then _____.

7. If a button falls off your coat, then _____.

8. If you find a bracelet on the playground, then _____.

9. If you drop your homework in a puddle, then _____.

10. If your pencil breaks while you are in class, then _____.

11. If you leave your Popsicle in the sun, then _____.

12. If you lose your lunch money on the way to school, then _____.

13. If the rain is coming in the window, then _____.

14. If you leave the lid off the Play-Doh overnight, then _____.

15. If your bicycle tire is flat, then _____.

16. If you drop a raw egg, then _____.

17. If your soccer team scores the most goals, then _____.

18. If there's a hole in your pocket and you put a dime in it, then _____.

19. If you eat hot soup without testing it first, then _____.

I.E.P. Goal: The student will give logical consequences for occurrences when presented with "If...then" statements with 90% or greater accuracy.

Note: This format may need to be taught initially by asking "what" questions.   Example: If it rains, then what will happen?

Association   28

 More Lesson 1

Name _____

Finish each sentence.

20. If you forget to walk the dog, then _____.

21. If you get a splinter in your finger, then _____.

22. If you find a letter in the mailbox with your name on it, then _____.

23. If you were nine on your last birthday, then _____.

24. If you go underwater with your mouth open, then _____.

25. If your team gets three outs while at bat, then _____.

26. If you feed your fish too much, then _____.

27. If today is Friday, then _____.

28. If this is Monday morning, then _____.

29. If you go to bed at midnight and have to get up at 6AM, then _____.

30. If you leave water running in the tub while you watch a TV show, then _____.

31. If your bicycle chain breaks, then _____.

32. If you stick a pin in a balloon, then _____.

33. If you are swinging outside and it starts to thunder, then _____.

34. If you are riding your bike and come to a stop sign, then _____.

35. If the songs on your tape recorder start to play too slowly, then _____.

36. If you put shampoo on your hair without wetting it, then _____.

37. If you rub a balloon on your head and put it on the wall, then _____.

38. If you don't take your medicine, then _____.

I.E.P. Goal: *The student will give logical consequences for occurrences when presented with "If...then" statements with 90% or greater accuracy.*

Note: This format may need to be taught initially by asking "what" questions. Example: If it rains, then what will happen?

Association   29

Name _____

Read each group of sentences.   Then, answer the questions.   The first one is done for you.

1. Terry left his roller skates at the bottom of the stairs.   His dad is walking down the stairs carrying a huge box.   What might happen?   *(He might fall.)*

2. James built a tower of 15 blocks.   When he put on the next block, the tower began to sway back and forth.   What might happen?

3. Tina built a sand castle at the beach.   A big wave was coming toward the shore.   What might happen?

4. Last night I heard a cat outside my window.   This morning the flower pot was smashed on the patio.   What happened?

5. My dad said, "Smile."   A bright light flashed.   What happened?

6. Angelo left his marbles on the rug and went upstairs.   His baby sister crawled into the room.   What might happen?

7. I put the popcorn in the microwave oven.   I took out the trash.   When I came back, I smelled something funny.   What happened?

8. A large truck was parked in front of the Ling's house.   Men were carrying out boxes and furniture and loading them in the truck.   Mrs. Ling was hugging a neighbor and crying. What was happening?

9. There were balloons on Joleen's mailbox.   A girl with a gift was ringing her doorbell. What was happening?

10. Mr. Barrett was in a hurry to unload the groceries and get to the basketball game.   He put the crackers in the freezer and the ice cream in the cabinet.   What will happen?

11. At the grocery store a woman wearing an apron was sweeping up a broken jar of pickles. What happened?

12. The man was very tall.   The doorway was very low.   He walked into the room very fast. What happened?

13. The phone rang.   I answered it.   I heard a steady buzzing noise in the phone.   What happened?

I.E.P. Goal: *When presented with facts concerning situations, the student will provide logical explanations for the occurrences with 90% or greater accuracy.*

Association   30

Name _____

Read each group of sentences.   Then, answer the questions.

14. No one in the classroom was talking.   All the students were sitting in their desks holding sharpened pencils.   There were no papers or books on any of the desks.   The teacher was giving a paper to each student.   What was happening?

15. Iris went to the library.   The man ahead of her was returning some books.   He was digging in his pockets for some change.   What was happening?

16. I bought a new sweatshirt in my size.   My mom washed it and I put it on.   The sleeves were too short.   What happened?

17. I woke up very early.   I heard a thump at the front door.   I saw a boy ride off on his bike. What happened?

18. The streets downtown were blocked off and there were no cars parked on the streets. People were lined up on both sides of the street.   They kept looking up the street, waiting for something.   What was happening?

19. Levi shook up the bottle of soda and left it on the counter.   His sister came into the kitchen and opened it.   What happened?

20. A young man wearing a suit and holding some flowers rang Beth's doorbell.   When she answered the door, Beth was wearing a long blue gown.   What was happening?

21. The door to the school building opened.   All the children came out and stood quietly in groups on the playground.   A short time after the bell rang they went back inside.   What happened?

22. A man in a wheelchair was being pushed out the front door of the hospital.   A woman with him was putting a basket of flowers and a suitcase in the car.   What was happening?

23. At a fast food restaurant, a customer brought an unwrapped sandwich back to the cashier. The cashier said, "I'm sorry.   We'll get you one with cheese."   What happened?

24. Jordan and Andrew went fishing.   They left early in the morning with their poles and a bucket of bait.   They came back a few hours later with their poles and an empty bucket. What happened?

25. While at the movie theater, the picture on the screen flickered and went out.   After a few minutes the lights came on.   Everyone stayed in their seats.   What happened?

I.E.P. Goal: When presented with facts concerning situations, the student will provide logical explanations for the occurrences with 90% or greater accuracy.

Association   31

Read each pair of words. Then, tell one way they are the same and one way they are different. The first one is done for you.

1. apple • orange
   (*same: you can eat both*)
   (*different: apples are red; oranges are orange*)

2. horse • cow

3. pen • pencil

4. car • motorcycle

5. soup • cereal

6. belt • ribbon

7. baby • puppy

8. screwdriver • knife

9. blanket • towel

10. soap • shampoo

11. merry-go-round • Ferris wheel

12. ice cream • pudding

13. rake • broom

14. glue • tape

15. pie • cake

16. coat • bathrobe

17. ketchup • mayonnaise

18. nail polish • paint

19. daisy • rose

20. ocean • lake

21. skunk • squirrel

22. envelope • paper bag

23. doll • puppet

24. elevator • escalator

25. doughnut • bagel

26. newspaper • magazine

27. photograph • statue

28. map • globe

29. handcuffs • bracelet

30. paper clip • staple

31. leopard • lion

32. typewriter • computer

33. Ping-Pong paddle • tennis racket

34. hotel • jail

35. judge • parent

36. building blocks • dice

37. poodle • dalmatian

38. frog • toad

I.E.P. Goal: The student will identify the similarities and differences for pairs of common nouns with 90% or greater accuracy.

Association

 **Lesson 4**

Name _____

Write the correct answers to the following questions about actions.   The first one is done for you.

1. What zips?   _zipper_

2. What cooks? _____

3. What flies? _____

4. What jumps? _____

5. What tastes? _____

6. What smells? _____

7. What touches? _____

8. What hears? _____

9. What digs? _____

10. What colors? _____

11. What grows? _____

12. What beeps? _____

13. What blows? _____

14. What chews? _____

15. What curls? _____

16. What races? _____

17. What ticks? _____

18. What writes? _____

19. What squirts? _____

20. What blinks? _____

21. What slices? _____

22. What aches? _____

23. What starts? _____

24. What shuts? _____

25. What boils? _____

26. What bites? _____

27. What tears? _____

28. What sweeps? _____

29. What sprays? _____

30. What splashes? _____

31. What flushes? _____

32. What breaks? _____

33. What squeaks? _____

34. What flashes? _____

35. What jingles? _____

36. What stops? _____

37. What marks? _____

38. What ties? _____

39. What stirs? _____

40. What beats? _____

I.E.P. Goal: When given questions involving actions, the student will give commonly associated agents with 90% or greater accuracy.

Name _____

Write the correct answers to the following questions about actions.

41. What claps? _____
42. What swings? _____
43. What falls? _____
44. What shakes? _____
45. What heats? _____
46. What sweetens? _____
47. What chills? _____
48. What winks? _____
49. What hisses? _____
50. What flows? _____
51. What cracks? _____
52. What licks? _____
53. What burns? _____
54. What records? _____
55. What weighs? _____
56. What blossoms? _____
57. What itches? _____
58. What yelps? _____
59. What protects? _____
60. What scoops? _____

61. What fizzes? _____
62. What covers? _____
63. What crunches? _____
64. What trots? _____
65. What cools? _____
66. What changes? _____
67. What scares? _____
68. What ends? _____
69. What measures? _____
70. What fastens? _____
71. What drains? _____
72. What sizzles? _____
73. What whinnies? _____
74. What entertains? _____
75. What spoils? _____
76. What fades? _____
77. What peels? _____
78. What leaks? _____
79. What shocks? _____
80. What bursts? _____

I.E.P. Goal: *When given questions involving actions, the student will give commonly associated agents with 90% or greater accuracy.*

Association   34

Name _____

Write what each thing does.   The first one is done for you.

1. What does a pen do?   _writes_____

2. What does a bib do?   _____

3. What does a comb do?   _____

4. What do gloves do?   _____

5. What does toothpaste do?   _____

6. What does an oven do?   _____

7. What does a horn do?   _____

8. What does glue do?   _____

9. What does a blanket do?   _____

10. What does a broom do?   _____

11. What does a key do?   _____

12. What does a hammer do?   _____

13. What do eyeglasses do?   _____

14. What does a watch do?   _____

15. What does the sun do?   _____

16. What does a kite do?   _____

17. What does a saw do?   _____

18. What does a shovel do?   _____

19. What does a refrigerator do?   _____

20. What does a drawer do?   _____

I.E.P. Goal: When given the names of objects, the student will name commonly associated actions with 90% or greater accuracy.

Association   35

 **More Lesson 5**

Name _____

Write what each thing does.

21. What does a button do? _____

22. What does a light do? _____

23. What does a Band-Aid do? _____

24. What does a radio do? _____

25. What does perfume do? _____

26. What do boots do? _____

27. What does a hanger do? _____

28. What does a piano do? _____

29. What does a ruler do? _____

30. What does the wind do? _____

31. What does an air conditioner do? _____

32. What does a tree do? _____

33. What does a nail do? _____

34. What does a calendar do? _____

35. What does a siren do? _____

36. What does a thermos do? _____

37. What does a leash do? _____

38. What does a pot holder do? _____

39. What does bug repellant do? _____

40. What does a fire extinguisher do? _____

I.E.P. Goal: When given the names of objects, the student will name commonly associated actions with 90% or greater accuracy.

Association   36

 **Lesson 6**

Name _____

Underline the answers to these questions comparing things.   The first one is started for you.

Comparison of Two Items

1. Which is smaller?

<u>ant</u>	mouse
chair	<u>cup</u>
pillow	earring
book	bed
newspaper	slice of bread

2. Which is prettier?

moth	butterfly
peacock	turkey
bouquet of flowers	can of worms
old bus	shiny car
new dress	doormat

3. Which is hotter?

air conditioner	heater
spring	summer
toaster	refrigerator
popcorn	ice cream
soup	pudding

4. Which is lighter?

piece of paper	piece of wood
sock	shoe
brick	newspaper
sponge	plate
dollar bill	quarter

5. Which is older?

grandmother	grandchild
son	father
daughter	mother
kitten	cat
cow	calf

I.E.P. Goal: Given characteristics in the form of questions, the student will choose the items which exhibit the specific characteristics with 90% or greater accuracy.

Association   37

Name _____

Underline the answers to these questions comparing things.

6. Which is slower?

    turtle   rabbit
    bicycle   motorcycle
    running   skipping
    boat   airplane
    bus   train

7. Which is sharper?

    scissors   comb
    paintbrush   knife
    rolling pin   axe
    shovel   broom
    toothpick   crayon

8. Which is sweeter?

    apple   lemon
    cookie   cracker
    pretzel   chocolate bar
    cake   bread
    wax   chewing gum

9. Which is longer?

    day   hour
    second   minute
    year   week
    month   day
    morning   hour

10. Which is rougher?

    towel   handkerchief
    bathtub   sidewalk
    paper towel   piece of plastic wrap
    alligator's back   cat's back
    rock   pine cone

I.E.P. Goal: *Given characteristics in the form of questions, the student will choose the items which exhibit the specific characteristics with 90% or greater accuracy.*

Association   38

Name _____

Underline the answers to these questions comparing things.

11. Which is noisier?	bulldozer	lawn mower
12. Which is cleaner?	old socks	new shoes
13. Which is shinier?	piece of foil	piece of construction paper
14. Which is taller?	eight-year-old boy	thirty-year-old woman
15. Which is softer?	marshmallows	lima beans
16. Which is juicier?	grape	peanut
17. Which is wider?	couch	front door
18. Which is thinner?	carrot	pretzel stick
19. Which is spicier?	popcorn	nachos
20. Which is weaker?	paper bag	cloth bag
21. Which is more sour?	pickle	celery
22. Which is fluffier?	cotton ball	eraser
23. Which is drier?	grass in the morning	sidewalk at noon
24. Which is less expensive?	lunch box	skateboard
25. Which gives more light?	flashlight	candle
26. Which makes a better pet?	skunk	rabbit
27. Which is calmer?	tornado	rainstorm
28. Which is harder to do?	make your bed	make a quilt
29. Which is more nutritious?	caramel	tomato
30. Which is trickier?	tying your shoe with one hand	ringing a doorbell with one finger

I.E.P. Goal: Given characteristics in the form of questions, the student will choose the items which exhibit the specific characteristics with 90% or greater accuracy.

Association

39

Name _____

Underline the answers to these questions comparing things.

Comparison of Three Items

1. Which is fastest?
   donkey
   race horse
   goat

2. Which smells best?
   tennis shoes
   gasoline
   soap

3. Which is quietest?
   running water
   writing
   playing the piano

4. Which breaks easiest?
   ball
   dish
   broom

5. Which is cutest?
   rat
   mole
   kitten

6. Which is largest?
   shark
   whale
   dolphin

7. Which is crispiest?
   bubble gum
   pudding
   cereal

8. Which is scariest?
   noise in the dark
   ringing phone
   ticking clock

9. Which holds the most?
   wallet
   purse
   briefcase

10. Which cleans best?
    detergent
    oil
    salt

11. Which bounces highest?
    marble
    Ping-Pong ball
    nickel

12. Which is longest?
    pencil
    yardstick
    ruler

13. Which is the most comfortable?
    suit
    pajamas
    jeans

14. Which needs the most care?
    mailbox
    lamp
    plant

15. Which is the most fun?
    shining shoes
    playing cards
    changing diapers

16. Which is the most slippery?
    icy sidewalk
    dirty floor
    new carpet

17. Which is silliest?
    jokes
    poems
    definitions

18. Which absorbs the most?
    book
    brick
    sponge

I.E.P. Goal: Given characteristics in the form of questions, the student will choose the items which exhibit the specific characteristics with 90% or greater accuracy.

Name _____

Underline the answers to these questions comparing things.

Comparison of Items Using Judgment

1. Which would you rather have?
   nickel
   five-dollar bill
   dollar
   dime

2. Which would you rather be?
   a student taking a test
   a mother washing the dishes
   a child at the beach
   a horse pulling a plow

3. Which would you rather taste?
   cough medicine
   chocolate syrup
   cooking oil
   soap

4. Which would you rather listen to?
   dripping faucet
   crying baby
   car alarm
   guitar

5. Which would you rather do?
   take out garbage
   play cards
   clean your room
   brush your teeth

6. Which is the most suitable outfit for school?
   pajamas
   bathing suit
   clown costume
   sweater and pants

7. Which thing is the most suitable to bring to school?
   pencil case
   hot dog
   Frisbee
   pillow

8. Which is the most entertaining?
   television show
   commercial
   telephone book
   place mat

9. Which is the most educational?
   amusement park
   museum
   telephone booth
   closet

10. Which is the most dangerous?
   putting on your socks
   crossing a busy highway
   watering house plants
   writing a book report

I.E.P. Goal: *Given characteristics in the form of questions, the student will choose the items which exhibit the specific characteristics with 90% or greater accuracy.*

Name _____

Underline the answers to these questions comparing things.

11. Which was invented first?

  covered wagon
  typewriter
  electric toaster
  bus

12. Which word is a baby most likely to say?

  absolutely
  cookie
  university
  seat belt

13. Which gift would a ten-year-old like the most?

  necktie
  blender
  skateboard
  filing cabinet

14. Which gift would an eight-year-old like the most?

  ice cube trays
  paint set
  battery
  shampoo

15. Which gift would a grandmother like the most?

  novel
  lawn mower
  rattle
  snake

16. Which gift would be best for a one-year-old child?

  scissors
  stuffed bear
  comic book
  yo-yo

17. In which store are you most likely to find a dictionary?

  hardware store
  shoe store
  book store
  video rental store

18. At which place are you most likely to find sausage?

  bakery
  barber shop
  butcher shop
  fruit stand

19. Which food needs to be kept the coldest?

  orange juice
  crackers
  bagels
  ice cream

20. Which thing are you most likely to see in the city?

  cattle crossing
  tractor
  ocean
  "Don't Walk" sign

I.E.P. Goal: *Given characteristics in the form of questions, the student will choose the items which exhibit the specific characteristics with 90% or greater accuracy.*

Lesson 7

Write the word for the thing described in each of these definitions.   The first one is done for you.

1. We use it to dry our hands after we wash them.   *towel* _____

2. It has a handle and we drink from it. _____

3. It's an orange vegetable that rabbits like. _____

4. Monkeys like this yellow fruit. _____

5. Children sit in these at school. _____

6. Birds are covered with these. _____

7. Babies wear these instead of underwear. _____

8. You turn it to open the door. _____

9. It is sweet and white and we sprinkle it on cereal. _____

10. We put candles on it on someone's birthday. _____

11. It sprays water on your head when you stand in the bathroom. _____

12. You must have one to unlock the door. _____

13. It's a sweet treat that we chew but do not swallow. _____

14. It's a large vehicle that carries many children to school. _____

15. We walk up these to get from the basement to the first floor. _____

16. This is something soft that we lay our heads on at night. _____

17. You eat this crunchy holder for ice cream. _____

18. It's what you lick and put on the corner of a letter. _____

19. It's the part of a bicycle you use to steer. _____

20. Farmers keep hay and animals in this building. _____

I.E.P. Goal: When given definitions, the student will identify the objects described with 90% or greater accuracy.

Name _____

Write the word for the thing described in each of these definitions.

21. This person cares for children when their parents go away. _____

22. These strings help hold your shoes on. _____

23. You find this liquid inside pens. _____

24. These are short hairs on the edge of your eyelids. _____

25. This part of your body bends between your wrist and shoulder. _____

26. This tool has a handle and you use it to clean up leaves. _____

27. A teacher teaches these people. _____

28. This is your mother's mother. _____

29. This is your father's brother. _____

30. It's another word for twelve o'clock in the daytime. _____

31. This brown furry animal builds dams in the water. _____

32. It's the brown outer edge of a slice of bread. _____

33. Cool water sprays from this and people get drinks from it. _____

34. You use this to cover a part of your body that's been hurt. _____

35. It's a long, flat piece of wood used to move a canoe through the water. _____

36. This long stick fits under a person's arm to help that person walk. _____

37. This round model of the earth shows the continents and oceans. _____

38. It's a baby's small bed that rocks back and forth. _____

39. This bed cover is made of colorful cloth squares stitched together. _____

40. This person rules over a courtroom and hears the cases. _____

I.E.P. Goal: When given definitions, the student will identify the objects described with 90% or greater accuracy.

Association

Write a word to finish each statement.   The first one is done for you.

1. Rocks are hard; pillows are _____soft_____ .

2. Lemons are yellow; tomatoes are _____ .

3. My eyes are for seeing; my ears are for _____ .

4. Pencils are for writing; brushes are for _____ .

5. If I'm hungry I go to the kitchen; if I'm sleepy I go to the _____ .

6. During the day we see the sun; at night we see the _____ .

7. Blocks are for building; scissors are for _____ .

8. Forks are used to eat; shovels are used to _____ .

9. You sleep on a bed; you swim in a _____ .

10. On my feet I wear socks; on my hands I wear _____ .

11. My waist has a belt; my neck has a _____ .

12. Bats live in a cave; birds live in a _____ .

13. Pigs' tails are curly; donkeys' tails are _____ .

14. A slice of bread is square; a plate is _____ .

15. A cow has a calf; a horse has a _____ .

16. A drawer has a handle; a door has a _____ .

17. I clean the floor with a broom; I clean the carpet with a _____ .

18. You guess a riddle; you ask a _____ .

19. Limes are sour; strawberries are _____ .

20. Babies wear booties; children wear _____ .

I.E.P. Goal: The student will complete analogous statements with 90% or greater accuracy.

Association   45

Name _____

Write a word to finish each statement.

21. A suitcase holds clothing; a wallet holds _____.

22. A square has four sides; a triangle has _____.

23. A siren wails; a bell _____.

24. A drugstore sells medicine; a post office sells _____.

25. Toast is dry; oranges are _____.

26. Cowboys use ropes; fire fighters use _____.

27. At noon it is light; at midnight it is _____.

28. Balloons have strings; corn dogs have _____.

29. Peanut butter is made from peanuts; jelly is made from _____.

30. Teachers work in a school; doctors work in a _____.

31. Water balloons have water; pens have _____.

32. Toilet paper comes on a roll; tissues come in a _____.

33. Football players score touchdowns; baseball players score _____.

34. Wolves are wild; hamsters are _____.

35. A lion roars; an owl _____.

36. A house has a roof; a box has a _____.

37. Carnivals have games; schools have _____.

38. Hockey players play on ice; basketball players play on a _____.

39. Dentists work on teeth; mechanics work on _____.

40. Bread has a crust; a picture has a _____.

I.E.P. Goal: The student will complete analogous statements with 90% or greater accuracy.

Association   46

More Lesson 8

Name _____

Write a word to finish each statement.

41. *Swim* is to *pool* as *skate* is to _____.

42. *Rafts* are to *water* as *sleds* are to _____.

43. *Toe* is to *foot* as *finger* is to _____.

44. *Whisper* is to *soft* as *yell* is to _____.

45. *Wagon* is to *pull* as *grocery cart* is to _____.

46. *Words* are to *spelling* as *numbers* are to _____.

47. *Baseball mitt* is to *hand* as *flippers* are to _____.

48. *Red* is to *color* as *vanilla* is to _____.

49. *Corn chip* is to *crisp* as *gelatin* is to _____.

50. *Turn* is to *corner* as *open* is to _____.

51. *Glasses* are to *eyes* as *braces* are to _____.

52. *Number* is to *telephone* as *address* is to _____.

53. *Swamp* is to *alligator* as *pond* is to _____.

54. *Chirp* is to *bird* as *howl* is to _____.

55. *Fry* is to *egg* as *mash* is to _____.

56. *Hide* is to *seek* as *lose* is to _____.

57. *Ball* is to *bounce* as *confetti* is to _____.

58. *Wring* is to *washcloth* as *fluff* is to _____.

59. *Diary* is to *private* as *newspaper* is to _____.

60. *Period* is to *sentence* as *stop sign* is to _____.

I.E.P. Goal: The student will complete analogous statements with 90% or greater accuracy.

Association
47

Specific Word Finding

Specific word finding tasks are used as a means of building vocabulary and word retrieval skills through association of certain words with common phrases and/or contextual cues. Stimulation of this area through repeated practice of word finding exercises will aid the student in recall of specific words in conversation when common associative cues are present, as well as enhancing speed of recall of common vocabulary words in conversation. Some students may have an adequate receptive knowledge of the vocabulary presented in this section, but need repeated drill work to retrieve this vocabulary for expressive use.

For some students, it may be helpful or necessary to provide initial phonemic cues for the target words when first working with these exercises. These cues should be gradually faded until word retrieval is accomplished solely with contextual cues.

Name _____

Fill in the blank to finish each phrase.   The first one is done for you.

1. _cut_____ the paper

2. _____ your lunch

3. _____ the lemonade

4. _____ the grass

5. _____ the baby

6. _____ a truck

7. _____ the ball

8. _____ with the crayons

9. _____ down the slide

10. _____ the stroller

11. _____ the dog

12. _____ a window

13. _____ the dishes

14. _____ your room

15. _____ the flowers

16. _____ on the swings

17. _____ the magazine

18. _____ your teeth

19. _____ on the airplane

20. _____ a horse

21. _____ in the chair

22. _____ a shower

23. _____ a postcard

24. _____ the newspapers

25. _____ the football game

26. _____ the candles

27. _____ the bowling ball

28. _____ your fingernails

29. _____ the parts together

30. _____ the picture

31. _____ the rug

32. _____ a doctor

33. _____ a present

34. _____ in the oven

35. _____ your money

36. _____ the tree

37. _____ the basketball game

38. _____ the bed

39. _____ down the hill

40. _____ with the chalk

I.E.P. Goal: *Given phrases which are missing initial verbs, the student will complete the phrases with appropriate verbs or verb phrases with 90% or greater accuracy.*

Specific Word Finding   49

More Lesson 1

Name _____

Fill in the blank to finish each phrase.

41. _____ the time

42. _____ the rice

43. _____ the soft fur

44. _____ the eggs

45. _____ your nose

46. _____ in the dirt

47. _____ the football

48. _____ the doorbell

49. _____ a banana

50. _____ the piano

51. _____ the drum

52. _____ the laundry

53. _____ the mask

54. _____ in the pond

55. _____ the suitcase

56. _____ the snow

57. _____ the apples

58. _____ the soccer ball

59. _____ a moving van

60. _____ the goggles

61. _____ down the tree

62. _____ on the trampoline

63. _____ on a beach

64. _____ a library book

65. _____ the chalkboard

66. _____ a comic book

67. _____ at the picture album

68. _____ the lullaby

69. _____ the sweater

70. _____ at the bus stop

71. _____ to the concert

72. _____ out the toothpaste

73. _____ under the umbrella

74. _____ the bow and arrow

75. _____ the tank with gas

76. _____ with an axe

77. _____ up the broken glass

78. _____ an answer

79. _____ your favorite flavor

80. _____ an appointment

I.E.P. Goal: Given phrases which are missing initial verbs, the student will complete the phrases with appropriate verbs or verb phrases with 90% or greater accuracy.

Name _____

For each situation, fill in the blank to finish the phrase.   The first one is done for you.

1. cold weather   a pair of _*mittens*_____

2. breakfast   a bowl of _____

3. birthday party   a piece of _____

4. dessert   a dish of _____

5. sickness   a spoonful of _____

6. pets   a can of _____

7. recipe   a cup of _____

8. school   a pile of _____

9. breakfast   a carton of _____

10. baking   a batch of _____

11. baby   a bottle of _____

12. party   a slice of _____

13. drink   a pitcher of _____

14. bakery   a loaf of _____

15. food   a bowl of _____

16. salad   a head of _____

17. clothing   a pair of _____

18. breakfast   a piece of _____

19. snack   a bag of _____

20. breakfast   a box of _____

*I.E.P. Goal: Given topics or situations and incomplete phrases which are missing final nouns, the student will
        complete the phrases with appropriate nouns with 90% or greater accuracy.*

Specific Word Finding   51

 **More Lesson 2**

Name _____

For each situation, fill in the blank to finish the phrase.

21. game   a deck of _____

22. hopscotch   a piece of _____

23. vegetables   a can of _____

24. bathing   a bar of _____

25. vacation   a suitcase full of _____

26. yardwork   a shovelful of _____

27. dinner   a forkful of _____

28. movies   a box of _____

29. home   a closetful of _____

30. laundry   a boxful of _____

31. picnic   a basketful of _____

32. baking   a stick of _____

33. cleanliness   a tube of _____

34. car   a gallon of _____

35. playroom   a box full of _____

36. weather   a drop of _____

37. art class   a box of _____

38. fruit   a bunch of _____

39. knitting   a ball of _____

40. baking   a bag of _____

I.E.P. Goal: Given topics or situations and incomplete phrases which are missing final nouns, the student will complete the phrases with appropriate nouns with 90% or greater accuracy.

Name _____

For each situation, fill in the blank to finish the phrase.

41. breakfast   a dozen _____

42. cookout   a package of _____

43. dairy farm   a bucket of _____

44. skier   a pair of _____

45. painter   a bucket of _____

46. library   a shelf of _____

47. fall   a pile of _____

48. sewing   a spool of _____

49. car   a quart of _____

50. butcher shop   a pound of _____

51. office building   a flight of _____

52. weather   a shovelful of _____

53. bank robber   a bag of _____

54. rowboat   a pair of _____

55. art class   a tube of _____

56. seasonings   a shaker of _____

57. school   a classroom of _____

58. grocery store   a sackful of _____

59. farm   a field of _____

60. camera   a roll of _____

*I.E.P. Goal: Given topics or situations and incomplete phrases which are missing final nouns, the student will
complete the phrases with appropriate nouns with 90% or greater accuracy.*

Name _____

For each situation, fill in the blank to finish the phrase.

61. forest   a group of _____

62. sewing   a yard of _____

63. kitchen   a set of _____

64. aquarium   a tank of _____

65. nighttime footwear   a pair of _____

66. bricklayer   a ton of _____

67. carpenter   a box full of _____

68. mouth   a row of _____

69. scuba diver   a tank of _____

70. farm   a bale of _____

71. broken leg   a pair of _____

72. beach   a pail of _____

73. school yearbook   a book full of _____

74. pharmacy   a bottle of _____

75. drink   a mug of _____

76. dentist office   a room full of _____

77. circus   a cageful of _____

78. bedroom   a chest of _____

79. animals   a flock of _____

80. fireplace   a load of _____

I.E.P. Goal: *Given topics or situations and incomplete phrases which are missing final nouns, the student will complete the phrases with appropriate nouns with 90% or greater accuracy.*

Name _____

Fill in the blank to finish each phrase.   The first one is done for you.

1. Mickey Mouse and *Minnie Mouse*

2. toothbrush and _____

3. ice cream and _____

4. comb and _____

5. shoes and _____

6. macaroni and _____

7. key and _____

8. table and _____

9. fork and _____

10. Bert and _____

11. bat and _____

12. coloring book and _____

13. boys and _____

14. up and _____

15. men and _____

16. pots and _____

17. come and _____

18. cup and _____

19. dogs and _____

20. pail and _____

21. hammer and _____

22. cars and _____

23. stop and _____

24. open and _____

25. eyes, nose, and _____

26. hat and _____

27. camera and _____

28. coat and _____

29. washer and _____

30. ladies and _____

31. clean and _____

32. buttons and _____

33. look and _____

34. grandma and _____

35. towel and _____

36. toast and _____

37. pencil and _____

38. sun and _____

39. socks and _____

40. cut and _____

I.E.P.Goal: *Given incomplete phrases containing conjunctions, the student will complete the phrases with appropriate words with 90% or greater accuracy.*

More

Name _____

Fill in the blank to finish each phrase.

41. brother and _____

42. big and _____

43. yes or _____

44. paper and _____

45. lightning and _____

46. doctor and _____

47. king and _____

48. front and _____

49. night and _____

50. black and _____

51. Jack and _____

52. taste and _____

53. rock and _____

54. Beauty and _____

55. left or _____

56. shampoo and _____

57. wrong or _____

58. tea and _____

59. chocolate or _____

60. fruits and _____

61. true or _____

62. stop, drop, and _____

63. lemons and _____

64. an arm and a _____

65. mustard and _____

66. pins and _____

67. markers and _____

68. hot dogs and _____

69. paper bags or _____

70. sheets and _____

71. nuts and _____

72. north and _____

73. city and _____

74. hot and _____

75. snap, crackle, and _____

76. add and _____

77. hit or _____

78. oil and _____

79. easel and _____

80. needle and _____

I.E.P. Goal: *Given incomplete phrases containing conjunctions, the student will complete the phrases with appropriate words with 90% or greater accuracy.*

Specific Word Finding

56

Name _____

Fill in the blank to finish each sentence.   The first one is done for you.

1. We looked at a _*picture*_____.

2. We sat in a _____.

3. We slept on a _____.

4. We washed a _____.

5. We ate the _____.

6. We sang the _____.

7. We poured the _____.

8. We knocked on the _____.

9. We saw our _____.

10. We caught the _____.

11. We cut the _____.

12. We did our _____.

13. We fed our _____.

14. We tied our _____.

15. We went to the _____.

16. We met a _____.

17. We walked the _____.

18. We cooked our _____.

19. We colored the _____.

20. We fixed the _____.

21. We listened to _____.

22. We made up the _____.

23. We jumped on a _____.

24. We spent our _____.

25. We frosted the _____.

26. We went on a _____.

27. We watched the _____.

28. We slipped on a _____.

29. We took the _____.

30. We baked the _____.

31. We found a _____.

32. We moved the _____.

33. We gave a _____.

34. We delivered the _____.

35. We wrote the _____.

36. We hung the _____.

37. We scrambled the _____.

38. We dried the _____.

39. We laughed at the _____.

40. We trimmed the _____.

I.E.P. Goal: Given sentences with incomplete verb phrases, the student will complete the sentences with appropriate nouns with 90% or greater accuracy.

Name _____

Fill in the blank to finish each sentence.

41. We won the _____.

42. We counted the _____.

43. We added the _____.

44. We taught the _____.

45. We smelled the _____.

46. We planted the _____.

47. We shut the _____.

48. We pushed the _____.

49. We locked the _____.

50. We played the _____.

51. We saved the _____.

52. We flew the _____.

53. We popped the _____.

54. We drove the _____.

55. We called the _____.

56. We built the _____.

57. We grew the _____.

58. We heard the _____.

59. We filled the _____.

60. We led the _____.

61. We repaired the _____.

62. We cleaned the _____.

63. We sold the _____.

64. We served the _____.

65. We picked up the _____.

66. We held the _____.

67. We left the _____.

68. We peeked around the _____.

69. We paid our _____.

70. We visited the _____.

71. We lifted the _____.

72. We checked out a _____.

73. We skated on _____.

74. We raked the _____.

75. We measured the _____.

76. We weighed the _____.

77. We donated _____.

78. We complimented our _____.

79. We attended the _____.

80. We elected the _____.

I.E.P. Goal: Given sentences with incomplete verb phrases, the student will complete the sentences with appropriate nouns with 90% or greater accuracy.

Specific Word Finding   58

 **Lesson 5**

Name _____

Fill in the blank to finish each sentence.   The first one is done for you.

1. Before we eat, we should wash our __*hands*_____.

2. In school, we learn to read a _____.

3. The fastest person will win the _____.

4. Before you go to bed, brush your _____.

5. My sister has to mow the _____.

6. We sleep in a _____.

7. We cut paper with _____.

8. Fish live in the _____.

9. To climb on the roof, you need a _____.

10. Use a mop to clean the _____.

11. When it snows, we wear boots on our _____.

12. Children who are just born are called _____.

13. Dad bakes bread in the _____.

14. Harry plays on a baseball _____.

15. The doctor gives sick people _____.

16. Hang your clean clothes in the _____.

17. To see in the dark, turn on the _____.

18. My dad gets to work by riding the _____.

19. A tree is cut down with a _____.

20. Kids like to go outside and ride their _____.

I.E.P. Goal: Given sentences which are missing final nouns, the student will complete the sentences with appropriate nouns with 90% or greater accuracy.

Specific Word Finding   59

More **Lesson 5**

Name _____

Fill in the blank to finish each sentence.

21. To let in some air, open the _____.

22. To keep their dogs in the yard, the Wilsons put up a _____.

23. Thomas missed his friend, so he wrote him a _____.

24. Every night after school, I do my _____.

25. In the summer, we go swimming in the _____.

26. Don't forget to lock the _____.

27. Before I do my homework, I sharpen my _____.

28. India's eye doctor said she might need to wear _____.

29. We keep the milk and juice cold in the _____.

30. Aaron couldn't get into his house because he had lost his _____.

31. Sue took pictures with a _____.

32. A carpenter puts wood together with nails and a _____.

33. To tell the time, look at a _____.

34. We eat dinner at the kitchen _____.

35. For strong bones and teeth, drink your _____.

36. My mom keeps her money and keys in her _____.

37. At the grocery store, you put the food in a _____.

38. Airplanes land and take off at the _____.

39. My sister checks out books at the _____.

40. When you camp outside, you sleep in a _____.

I.E.P. Goal: Given sentences which are missing final nouns, the student will complete the sentences with appropriate nouns with 90% or greater accuracy.

Name _____

Write the word in the blank for each definition.   The first one is done for you.

1. Babies drink it.   _milk_____

2. Kids ride them.   _____

3. We sit in them.   _____

4. Teachers write on them.   _____

5. It's the room we sleep in.   _____

6. It's something we read.   _____

7. It lays eggs.   _____

8. We call our friends with it.   _____

9. We wear them on our feet.   _____

10. You use it to cut your food.   _____

11. You use one when it rains.   _____

12. We check out books at this place.   _____

13. Dinner is cooked in this room.   _____

14. We ride them across the water.   _____

15. They run on tracks and rails.   _____

16. We use one to dig a hole.   _____

17. We keep food cold in it.   _____

18. I wear one to tell the time.   _____

19. You dry off with one after you take a bath.   _____

20. We use them when we sneeze.   _____

I.E.P. Goal: Given definitions, the student will identify the objects described with 90% or greater accuracy.

Specific Word Finding   61

Name _____

Write the word in the blank for each definition.

21. People wear them to see better.   _____

22. It's used to clean teeth.   _____

23. This is the person in charge of a school.   _____

24. You catch them with a rod and reel.   _____

25. They give us medicine when we're sick.   _____

26. Rabbits eat these orange vegetables.   _____

27. This is the body part that helps you hear.   _____

28. This is a large, gray animal with big ears and tusks.   _____

29. It shows the days of the week.   _____

30. You wear this piece of jewelry around your neck.   _____

31. You turn it to open the door.   _____

32. This small insect lives in a hive.   _____

33. We put mail in them.   _____

34. You take a bath in one.   _____

35. You use this to wash your body.   _____

36. Pet birds live in these.   _____

37. This person flies airplanes.   _____

38. These are tall with branches and are found outside.   _____

39. A dog wears this around its neck.   _____

40. This small, fuzzy insect turns into a butterfly.   _____

I.E.P. Goal: Given definitions, the student will identify the objects described with 90% or greater accuracy.

Name _____

List the items you need to do each of these things.   The first one is done for you.

1. tie your shoe   (*shoe, shoelaces*)

2. brush your teeth

3. sweep the floor

4. comb your hair

5. color a picture

6. eat a bowl of soup

7. get dressed for bed

8. read a bedtime story

9. throw away garbage

10. wash your dog

11. eat some cereal

12. go swimming

13. buy your lunch

14. dig a hole

15. get to school

16. slice cheese

17. wrap a present

18. get up on time

19. cover your windows at night

20. call an ambulance

21. take your temperature

22. feed a newborn baby

23. write a note

24. feed the dog

25. mow the lawn

26. mail a birthday card

27. make a peanut butter sandwich

28. change the bed

29. wash the car

30. fly a kite

31. blow your nose

32. make hot chocolate

33. serve hot dogs

34. cut down a tree

35. tell the time

36. see how much you weigh

37. watch Saturday cartoons

38. remove fallen leaves from the lawn

39. pack clothes for a trip

40. listen to music

I.E.P. Goal: Given tasks, the student will name the items necessary for completion of the tasks with 90% or greater accuracy.

Name _____

List the items you need to do each of these things.

41. water the lawn

42. unlock the door

43. wash your clothes

44. catch a baseball

45. keep dry in the rain

46. make brownies

47. raise the flag

48. fly on an airplane

49. change a ceiling light bulb

50. float on a pond

51. go to a movie

52. play a drum

53. do your homework

54. check the spelling of a word

55. have a snowball fight

56. measure how tall someone is

57. build a brick wall

58. fix a broken leg

59. fix a broken wing on a toy airplane

60. sing a song

61. do addition problems

62. make a tape recording

63. make a long-distance call

64. hit a home run

65. buy a dress

66. go grocery shopping

67. frost a cake

68. get a splinter out of your finger

69. check out a book

70. clean the windows

71. make a tossed salad

72. catch a fish

73. grill a steak

74. put a bike together

75. cook a turkey

76. paddle your boat

77. grow flowers

78. kick a field goal

79. go on a picnic

80. rescue a cat from a tree

I.E.P. Goal: Given tasks, the student will name the items necessary for completion of the tasks with 90% or greater accuracy.

Specific Word Finding   64

Grammar

Grammar represents the student's ability to use semantic units in specific patterns, or syntactic units, to convey meaning.   This communication skill is based on appropriate reception, discrimination, association, and memory skills which enable appropriate encoding of semantic and syntactic units and their relationships in providing effective communication skills.   Through stimulation of the grammatical forms, the student becomes familiar with patterns to use in expressing thoughts, actions, and feelings.

Name _____

Circle the correct pronoun for each sentence.   The first one is done for you.

1. (I, Me) am going home.

2. (She, Her) walks the dog.

3. (Them, You) will help the man.

4. (He, Him) knocked it down.

5. (Her, She) is my best friend.

6. (It, Him) won't be easy to find.

7. (Her, It) is a toy car.

8. (You, Him) can go tomorrow.

9. (Us, We) went shopping this afternoon.

10. (They, Us) came for a visit.

11. (Him, He) practiced playing the piano.

12. (Us, We) brushed our teeth.

13. (We, Us) won't know until later.

14. (Her, She) is climbing the monkey bars.

15. (Us, We) slid down the hill.

16. (Me, I) took my lunch to school.

17. (You, It) are my sister's teacher.

18. (She, Her) finished the homework paper.

19. (Me, I) am writing a letter to my friend.

20. (It, They) went on a field trip to the zoo.

21. (Her, You) made my appointment.

22. (They, Him) went for a hike on the trail.

23. (Their, They) will have a picnic in the park.

24. (Him, He) shampooed his hair.

25. (You, It) are the first person in line.

26. (We, Us) will hang her picture on the board.

27. (It, They) was almost eight o'clock.

28. (His, He) will help her with the project.

29. (My, I) can't go to the game tonight.

30. (They, Them) are going grocery shopping.

31. (I, Me) had an argument with my friend.

32. (It, They) was on sale.

33. (Him, He) wore new boots to school.

34. (They, Them) are in the talent show.

35. (It, Them) was given to him as a treat.

36. (He, Him) and his brother played video games.

37. (Her, She) and her best friend listen to the radio.

38. George and (I, me) will buy tickets for the carnival.

I.E.P. Goal: The student will select the correct subjective pronouns in sentences with 90% or greater accuracy.

Grammar

Name _____

Circle the correct pronoun for each sentence.   The first one is done for you.

1. (His, Him) dog is small.

2. (My, Me) new jeans have pockets.

3. (Yours, Your) book bag is green.

4. (Their, Them) parents will pick up the boys.

5. (Our, We) neighbors are out of town.

6. (My, Mine) ankle hurts.

7. (His, Hims) garden was big.

8. (They, Their) tree has more apples than mine.

9. (Him, His) brother came to the carnival.

10. (Her, She) bedroom is a mess.

11. (Their, Him) car has new tires.

12. (Us, Our) road was paved this morning.

13. (Her, She) wallet was full of pictures.

14. (He, His) birthday is in a few weeks.

15. (Theirs, Our) teacher graded the papers.

16. (My, I) mom brought the library book to school.

17. (She, Her) thumb was burned.

18. (We, Our) football team won the game.

19. (Their, They) memories were all good ones.

20. (Your, Yours) gym shorts are in the dryer.

21. (Me, My) watch stopped working.

22. (They, Our) class project is the best.

23. (It, Their) lunch is ready.

24. (His, He) pen ran out of ink.

25. Kim turned in (her, she) homework.

26. We cancelled (they, our) trip to the store.

27. Brian put the books in (his, he) desk.

28. Nate married (mine, my) sister's friend.

29. She fell and skinned (her, she) knee.

30. I have (yours, your) winning ticket.

31. You can leave when (you, your) bus comes.

32. I can't believe I lost (my, mine) jacket.

33. Gary will work on (his, hims) car.

34. Marlene wanted to talk to (her, she) mother.

35. Ned happened to walk past (theirs, their) house.

36. The boy slipped and hurt (his, her) head.

37. The dentist will clean (her, she) teeth on Friday.

I.E.P. Goal: The student will select the correct possessive pronouns in sentences with 90% or greater accuracy.

Grammar   67

Circle the correct pronoun for each sentence.   The first one is done for you.

1. I saw (she, (her)) in the store.

2. Give (me, I) a chance.

3. Cal called (he, him) last night.

4. Jerry fixed (her, she) some coffee.

5. Dan will load the van for (us, ours).

6. Hannah borrowed some CDs from (him, he).

7. Finally, we said goodnight to (them, they).

8. We ordered a pizza for (his, him).

9. The football belongs to (us, we).

10. We helped (them, they) take the books to the library.

11. Mom paid (them, they) to walk the dog.

12. Donny asked (I, me) to go to the movies.

13. The waiter served (they, them) the dessert.

14. My brother tried to scare (we, us) in the backyard.

15. The football player fell on (him, he) during the game.

16. Lynette will give (me, I) a ride to the mall.

17. Hal sold his rock collection to (her, she).

18. The neighbors asked (we, us) to watch their new video.

19. Penny wouldn't talk to (they, her).

20. Doug's father gave (him, he) the back door key.

21. Drew went with (them, they) to the swimming pool.

22. We watched (us, them) skate around the pond.

23. I helped (us, him) with his homework.

24. Lissa begged (she, her) not to go.

25. Greg danced with (we, us) at the party.

26. Travis broke the bad news to (them, they).

27. The new racket was given to (him, he).

28. The red ties made (us, we) look great!

29. Jaymie didn't know it was Megan and (I, me).

30. Jake grew pumpkins for all of (they, them).

31. Carol and Pepe couldn't find Jim and (I, me).

32. Tanisha told the story to her mom and (they, them).

33. The decision was up to (him, he) and me.

34. The notebooks were for (she, her) and (me, I).

35. We bought jackets for (him, he) and (her, she).

I.E.P. Goal: The student will select the correct objective pronouns in sentences with 90% or greater accuracy.

Name _____

Change each underlined noun or noun phrase to a pronoun.   The first one is done for you.

1. <u>Max</u> is my brother.   _He_____

2. <u>Mom</u> likes to fly on airplanes.   _____

3. <u>My friends</u> all sat in the first row.   _____

4. Mr. Hill scraped dirt off <u>the shovel</u>.   _____

5. <u>Sherry</u> stuffed her hair in her cap.   _____

6. <u>The fan</u> stopped when the lights went off.   _____

7. Sue gave the bracelet to <u>Amanda</u>.   _____

8. <u>The teachers</u> said the treats were delicious.   _____

9. Mrs. Davis loaned her pencil to <u>Zed</u>.   _____

10. <u>Brett</u> wrote his name for the first time.   _____

11. <u>Mr. Thompson</u> showed us how to do the exercises.   _____

12. I went back to school with <u>Toby</u>.   _____

13. <u>The brown bear</u> lives at the zoo.   _____

14. <u>Emily</u> jumped rope with Martina.   _____

15. <u>Larry</u> ate gelatin for dessert.   _____

16. <u>Natalie</u> scrubbed the bathrooms.   _____

17. <u>The bowling ball</u> rolled down the alley.   _____

18. <u>Jason</u> took the picture that won the contest.   _____

19. <u>The toys</u> were stacked neatly on the bookshelves.   _____

20. <u>That book</u> was the best mystery I've ever read.   _____

I.E.P. Goal: The student will change nouns and noun phrases to pronouns in sentences with 90% accuracy.

 **More Lesson 4**

Name _____

Change each underlined noun or noun phrase to a pronoun.

21. I can throw a baseball farther than <u>Heath</u>. _____

22. <u>Douglas</u> wrote in his journal. _____

23. <u>My friends</u> love to play with markers and paper. _____

24. <u>Maureen</u> and her sister wrote a poem. _____

25. <u>Dan</u> and his friend walked down the alley. _____

26. <u>Jan and Bryce</u> are my best friends. _____

27. <u>Jed and I</u> love to dive. _____

28. Make sure you tell <u>Patrick and Jeremy</u>. _____

29. <u>Sarah and Brian</u> listened to music all night. _____

30. <u>Hot dogs and hamburgers</u> are great at picnics. _____

31. <u>Jim and I</u> went riding in the park. _____

32. <u>Jose and Maria</u> set up a lemonade stand. _____

33. Mrs. Tyke is going to call <u>Josh and me</u>. _____

34. That puppy belongs to <u>Ann and Katie</u>. _____

35. The jackets were given to <u>Kathy, Jodi, and Amber</u>. _____

36. Rick returned <u>the book</u> to the library. _____

37. Please put <u>the gifts</u> in the bag. _____

38. Ask <u>Jay</u> if he can come play. _____

39. The chimney sweep cleaned <u>Krystal's</u> fireplace. _____

40. I need to give <u>Judy</u> ten paper clips. _____

I.E.P. Goal: The student will change nouns and noun phrases to pronouns in sentences with 90% accuracy.

Name _____

Change each underlined noun or noun phrase to a pronoun.

41. Let's have <u>Pat and Brannon</u> come along! _____

42. <u>Mother and I</u> had an argument. _____

43. The baseball hit <u>Jan</u> in the knee. _____

44. Grandma let <u>my cousin and me</u> go outside. _____

45. Black pepper makes <u>Cal</u> sneeze. _____

46. Don't count <u>your chickens</u> before they hatch! _____

47. The cab driver helped <u>Tucker and me</u> fix the tire. _____

48. <u>Sandy and I</u> made apple cinnamon muffins. _____

49. <u>My sister and I</u> raked the leaves. _____

50. <u>Scott's and my</u> plan backfired. _____

51. The store in <u>Bob's</u> neighborhood closes at five. _____

52. Please pick <u>your toys</u> up before you go to bed. _____

53. <u>My aunt</u> tried on <u>Marla's</u> coat. _____

54. <u>Shane's</u> mom took <u>Shane and his friends</u> out for pizza. _____

55. <u>Mark and I</u> went over to see <u>Holly</u>. _____

56. <u>My father</u> likes to read <u>the newspaper</u>. _____

57. <u>Dad and I</u> put meatballs in <u>the spaghetti sauce</u>. _____

58. <u>Mrs. Hillman</u> and her family donated <u>the books</u> to the library. _____

59. <u>Brooke and her mom</u> left the dogs with <u>Scott and me</u>. _____

60. <u>Adam</u> gave <u>the ring</u> to <u>Wendy</u>. _____

I.E.P. Goal: The student will change nouns and noun phrases to pronouns in sentences with 90% accuracy.

Grammar   71

Circle the correct word to complete each sentence.   The first one is done for you.

1. The baby elephant was (smaller, smallest) than its mother.

2. David is the (taller, tallest) boy in his family.

3. John's snow fort was (bigger, biggest) than mine.

4. I'm feeling (sicker, sickest) today than yesterday.

5. The bread we just made is the (fresher, freshest).

6. This is the (hotter, hottest) place I've ever been!

7. She is the (quieter, quietest) student in study hall.

8. This radio is (cheaper, cheapest) than that one.

9. The (littler, littlest) gift was the best of all.

10. That program is (funnier, funniest) every time I see it.

11. Mia is the (friendlier, friendliest) person I know.

12. An ice cube is (colder, coldest) than water.

13. The red team was (faster, fastest) than the blue team.

14. Bill had the (dirtier, dirtiest) face in the room.

15. This test is (easier, easiest) than the last test.

16. These crackers are (crispier, crispiest) than those.

17. I want the (softer, softest) tissue you have.

18. Carla sat in the (smaller, smallest) chair in the room.

19. Get the (nicer, nicest) fabric you can find.

20. That jar of peanut butter is the (crunchier, crunchiest).

I.E.P. Goal: The student will choose the correct comparative or superlative forms in sentences with 90% or greater accuracy.

Circle the correct word to complete each sentence.

21. This sock is (cleaner, cleanest) than that one.

22. His pencil is (sharper, sharpest) than mine.

23. The ride to the village was (rougher, roughest) than I expected.

24. The millionaire is the (richer, richest) person in town.

25. It was (darker, darkest) in the house than it was outside.

26. That is the (more, most) spaghetti I've ever seen Eddie eat.

27. A boulder is (heavier, heaviest) than a rock.

28. Sam's father was (prouder, proudest) than a peacock!

29. Mrs. Trover was (busier, busiest) than a bee.

30. Pete's yogurt was the (tastier, tastiest).

31. Mr. Gooding was the (angrier, angriest) Jake had ever seen.

32. A feather is (lighter, lightest) than a purse.

33. Adrian's room is the (messier, messiest) one in the apartment.

34. She found the (tinier, tiniest) speck of dust on the ledge.

35. Keesha is the (louder, loudest) one in our group.

36. Lisa always comes in the (later, latest).

37. Gray is a (lighter, lightest) color than black.

38. Andrea is my (better, best) friend.

39. The passageway was (narrower, narrowest) than I remembered it.

40. That dog is the (uglier, ugliest) I've ever seen.

I.E.P. Goal: The student will choose the correct comparative or superlative forms in sentences with 90% or greater accuracy.

Name _____

Circle the correct word to complete each sentence.

41. Jim arrived (earlier, earliest) than Samantha.

42. The little boy was (quicker, quickest) than his mom.

43. This is the (stickier, stickiest) glue I've ever used.

44. Tree bark is (rougher, roughest) than boards.

45. Juan's father is (older, oldest) than he.

46. The (shorter, shortest) bat in the group is Kevin's.

47. The (skinnier, skinniest) kid in our club squeezed through the hole in the fence.

48. Kathryn's bed is (softer, softest) than the one in the guest room.

49. He is the (neatest, most neatest) child in the preschool.

50. The hamburgers were (better, best) than the hot dogs.

51. Toni wanted the (shinier, shiniest) penny in the wallet.

52. An airplane can fly (higher, highest) than a kite.

53. He is the (sneakier, sneakiest) person I've ever met!

54. Phil likes his Chinese food (spicier, spiciest) than Carmen.

55. Her job was (more difficult, most difficult) than his.

56. Mr. Luciani is the (most honest, honestest) person I know.

57. The wolf was the (more ferocious, most ferocious) animal in the zoo.

58. A pear is (more nutritious, most nutritious) than a candy bar.

59. The (tighter, tightest) the string on the guitar, the higher the pitch.

60. He is the (lesser, least) likely person to win.

I.E.P. Goal: *The student will choose the correct comparative or superlative forms in sentences with 90% or greater accuracy.*

74

Name _____

Fill in the blank with the plural form of the noun in the first sentence.   The first one is done for you.

1. I have a can.   You have three __cans_____.

2. I have a boat.   We have three _____.

3. I have a cat.   You have four _____.

4. I have a spoon.   You have twelve _____.

5. I have a coat.   They have two _____.

6. I have an eraser.   You have four _____.

7. I have a penny.   You have a handful of _____.

8. I have a bicycle.   You have two _____.

9. I have a doctor.   They have three _____.

10. I have a duck.   You have three _____.

11. I have a carrot.   You have several _____.

12. I have a bed.   You have many _____.

13. I have a sister.   They have two _____.

14. I have a basket.   You have lots of _____.

15. I have a closet.   You have a couple of _____.

16. I have a table.   They have three _____.

17. I have a telephone.   You have three _____.

18. I have a key.   You have a few _____.

19. I have a rock.   You have twenty _____.

20. I have a broom.   They have two _____.

I.E.P. Goal: The student will supply plural forms for regular nouns in sentences with 90% or greater accuracy.

 More **Lesson 6**

Name _____

Fill in the blank with the plural form of the noun in the first sentence.

21. I have a nail.   They have a dozen _____.

22. I have a camera.   You have two _____.

23. I have a puppet.   You have three _____.

24. I have a mask.   We have two _____.

25. I have a bee.   You have twenty-five _____.

26. I have a ruler.   You have three _____.

27. I have a straw.   We have two _____.

28. I have a whistle.   They have several _____.

29. I have a bear.   You have three _____.

30. I have a tractor.   They have two _____.

31. I have a pumpkin.   You have three _____.

32. I have a rabbit.   You have many _____.

33. I have a drum.   You have three _____.

34. I have a room.   You have six _____.

35. I have a pocket.   You have four _____.

36. I have a window.   They have six _____.

37. I have a notebook.   You have several _____.

38. I have a cavity.   You have four _____.

39. I have a van.   You have two _____.

40. I have a helmet.   They have three _____.

I.E.P. Goal: The student will supply plural forms for regular nouns in sentences with 90% or greater accuracy.

Grammar

76

 **More** **Lesson 6**

Name _____

Fill in the blank with the plural form of the noun in the first sentence.

41. I have a canoe. You have three _____.

42. I have a battery. You have four _____.

43. I have a sponge. They have six _____.

44. I have a couch. You have three _____.

45. I have a mailbox. They have two _____.

46. I have a watch. You have two _____.

47. I have a toothbrush. You have four _____.

48. I have a wrench. You have a box full of _____.

49. I ride a bus. You ride two _____.

50. I see a nurse. You see three _____.

51. I have a patch. You have three _____.

52. I have a dish. You have a set of _____.

53. I have a match. You have a book of _____.

54. I have a jar of glue. You have two _____.

55. I have a bottle of shampoo. You have three _____.

56. I have a handful of candy. You have two _____.

57. I have a bunch of grapes. You have two _____.

58. I have a piece of chalk. You have eight _____.

59. I have a jug of milk. You have two _____.

60. I have a pair of socks. You have six _____.

I.E.P. Goal: The student will supply plural forms for regular nouns in sentences with 90% or greater accuracy.

Grammar   **77**

Complete each sentence by circling the correct word.   The first one is done for you.

1. The (mans, (men)) heard the car start.

2. The kids hung their (foots, feet) in the water.

3. The (womans, women) walked around the corner.

4. All the (children, childs) caught the bus.

5. The (elfs, elves) put the toys in the sack.

6. I saw the (mice, mouses) scurry across the floor.

7. We caught ten (fish, fishes) yesterday.

8. Laura put all the materials on the (bookshelfs, bookshelves).

9. The (deers, deer) were blinded by the light.

10. The cow had three (calves, calfs).

11. Pete loves to read books about (wolfs, wolves).

12. The goats fell and hurt their (hoofs, hooves).

13. Lenny lost all of his (tooths, teeth).

14. The ten (geese, gooses) are loose in the yard.

15. Wouldn't it be nice to have several (lifes, lives)?

16. The four (sheeps, sheep) walked down the mountainside.

17. The guests needed six bars of (soap, soaps).

18. Naomi wanted fifteen pieces of (fruits, fruit).

19. In the fall, we rake (leaves, leafs).

20. There are a lot of (moose, mooses) in Alaska.

I.E.P. Goal: The student will select the correct irregular plural forms in sentences with 90% or greater accuracy.

Fill in the blank with the plural form of the underlined word in the first sentence. The first one is done for you.

1. I lost my <u>tooth</u>. I lost three __*teeth*_____.

2. The cow had a <u>calf</u>. The cow had two _____.

3. The <u>man</u> mowed his yard. The three _____ mowed their yards.

4. Jodi wears a <u>scarf</u>. Jodi wears two _____.

5. I sharpened a <u>knife</u>. I sharpened eight _____.

6. The <u>thief</u> robbed the bank. The two _____ robbed the bank.

7. I caught a <u>leaf</u>. I caught five _____.

8. I hurt my <u>foot</u>. I hurt both _____.

9. The man called his <u>wife</u>. The two men called their _____.

10. I gave him <u>half</u>. I gave him both _____.

11. I baked a <u>loaf</u> of bread. I baked two _____ of bread.

12. I saw the <u>goose</u>. I saw seven _____.

13. I met a <u>woman</u>. I met five _____.

14. I saw the <u>mouse</u> go in the hole. I saw four _____ go in the hole.

15. I played with the <u>child</u>. I played with all the _____.

16. I took a picture of the <u>deer</u>. I took a picture of four _____.

17. There is a lost <u>sheep</u>. There is a flock of _____.

18. The cart is pulled by the <u>ox</u>. The cart is pulled by four _____.

19. I caught a <u>fish</u>. I caught four _____.

20. The carpenter put up one <u>shelf</u>. The carpenter put up three _____.

I.E.P. Goal: The student will supply plural forms for irregular nouns in sentences with 90% or greater accuracy.

Circle the word that correctly completes each sentence.   The first one is done for you.

1. We (is, (are)) going to the museum.

2. I (am, is) late for school.

3. The railroad tracks (was, were) covered with snow.

4. He (is, are) laughing at the joke.

5. It (was, were) a great parade.

6. The grocery store (was, were) open on the holiday.

7. April (has, have) a bad cold.

8. The bushes (was, were) trimmed.

9. The birds (was, were) building a nest.

10. You (are, is) my best friend.

11. We (was, were) happy with the news.

12. (Is, Are) you coming to the party?

13. The circus (is, are) coming to town.

14. The butcher (has, have) a lot of meat.

15. (Was, Were) you shopping this afternoon?

16. They (was, were) timing the swim meet.

17. (Is, Are) you going to the fair?

18. (Has, Have) Julia put on her makeup?

19. Audrey and Samuel (has, have) many pets.

20. (Has, Have) they called yet?

21. (Was, Were) Laura coming to play?

22. Luke's cousins (was, were) visiting their grandma.

23. (Has, Have) you lost a tooth yet?

24. Daniel (has, have) four trucks.

25. (Am, Are) you sure you aren't coming?

26. (Is, Are) Justin going to miss the meeting?

27. (Was, Were) her dog brown and white?

28. Martina (dive, dives) into the pool.

29. Holly (walk, walks) home from school.

30. The children (wave, waves) goodbye.

31. Birds (fly, flies) in the sky.

32. Andre (float, floats) on the pond.

33. Be careful because sometimes the dog (bite, bites).

34. Joleen (drive, drives) the car.

35. The rabbits (hop, hops) through the field.

36. Francis (paddle, paddles) the boat downstream.

37. Jesse (kick, kicks) the ball.

I.E.P. Goal: The student will choose singular or plural verb forms based on the context of sentences with 90% or greater accuracy.

Circle the word that correctly completes each sentence

38. Tim (dig, digs) in the sandbox.

39. The kids (sleep, sleeps) late on Saturday.

40. Fern (tie, ties) her shoes.

41. The children (cut, cuts) the paper strips.

42. He (zip, zips) his pants.

43. Mrs. Humphries (write, writes) on the chalkboard.

44. They (comb, combs) their hair.

45. Beth (buckle, buckles) her belt.

46. Margarita (like, likes) to jump rope.

47. Anthony (cry, cries) at night.

48. We (read, reads) the books.

49. They (sit, sits) on the bench.

50. Wally (hang, hangs) from the monkey bars.

51. The mother (carry, carries) the baby.

52. The students (run, runs) around the track.

53. The man (sweep, sweeps) the floor.

54. We (swim, swims) every Tuesday.

55. The nursery (use, uses) many diapers.

56. The child (check, checks) out the book.

57. The cashiers (weigh, weighs) the produce.

58. The family (eat, eats) their dinner.

59. Oprah (see, sees) better with her glasses.

60. The kids (talk, talks) on the sidewalk.

61. The babies (stack, stacks) the blocks.

62. The workers (pour, pours) the concrete.

63. We (drink, drinks) from the water fountain.

64. My mom (hug, hugs) me all the time.

65. I (go, goes) to bed at 8 o'clock.

66. The children (knock, knocks) on the door.

67. Arthur (roll, rolls) the log down the hill.

68. Doctors (treat, treats) sick people.

69. Corey (yell, yells) when he gets his allergy shots.

70. Each of the students (take, takes) a turn.

71. Both of my sisters (is, are) coming for the next show.

72. I (deserve, deserves) to win the award.

73. The acrobat (balance, balances) on the high wire.

I.E.P. Goal: **The student will choose singular or plural verb forms based on the context of sentences with 90% or greater accuracy.**

Grammar   81

Name _____

The first sentence in each numbered item below describes an event. Fill in the blank of the second sentence that tells that the event has already happened. The first one is done for you.

1. Ned is going to brush his teeth. These are the teeth he _brushed_____.

2. I am going to tie my shoes. These are the shoes I _____.

3. Ben is going to comb his hair. His hair looked great after he _____ it.

4. Margo is going to jump rope. This is the rope she _____.

5. Jim is going to button his shirt. This is the shirt he _____.

6. The baby is going to crawl across the floor. This is the floor where she

   _____.

7. You are going to mail some letters. This is the mailbox where you

   _____ the letters.

8. Jason is going to walk to school. This is the way he _____.

9. The rabbits are going to hop through the brush. Those are the rabbits that

   _____ by yesterday.

10. Terry is going to color a picture. This is the picture he _____.

11. We were going to listen to the teacher. She gave us a prize because we all

    _____.

12. Joel is going to mow four yards. The Smith's lawn is the one he _____ first.

13. Jan is going to tape the movie. This is the movie she _____.

14. Ron is going to rake the yard. The side yard is the one he _____.

15. The children are going to play games. These are the games they _____.

I.E.P. Goal: *The student will supply regular past tense verb forms based on the context of sentences with 90% or greater accuracy.*

Name _____

The first sentence in each numbered item below describes an event.   Fill in the blank of the second sentence that tells that the event has already happened.

16. Haley is going to zip her jacket.   Her zipper got stuck when she

    _____ it.

17. The kids are going to roll down the hills.   They _____ down the hills in Highland Park.

18. We are going to lock the doors.   Those doors were already _____.

19. Lana is going to peel a banana.   She gave me the banana she _____.

20. Ken is going to pour lemonade from the pitcher.   He _____ the lemonade for the children.

21. Let's go to the house Juan will paint.   Here is the house he _____.

22. Evan bounces the basketball.   Yesterday, Evan _____ the basketball.

23. Amanda can call a friend on the phone.   Marcia is the friend Amanda

    _____.

24. Cindy was trying not to smile.   She couldn't help it when she finally _____.

25. Patti laughs a lot.   She _____ at the clown's tricks.

26. The mechanic works on engines.   This is the engine he _____ on.

27. Horses gallop across the field.   Last week the spotted horse _____ across that same field.

28. Dave races cars for a living.   This car is the one he _____ last Wednesday.

29. Phil enjoys jogging.   This is the track where he _____.

30. Kirk has to wait for a ride.   This is where he _____.

I.E.P. Goal: *The student will supply regular past tense verb forms based on the context of sentences with 90% or greater accuracy.*

Name _____

The first sentence in each numbered item below describes an event. Fill in the blank of the second sentence that tells that the event has already happened.

31. Troy rarely misses a football game. However, Friday's game was one he

    _____ .

32. Ned lives upstairs from her. Last month, he _____ in a different apartment.

33. The kennel cares for dogs and cats. The kennel_____ for my dog while I was gone.

34. You must lick stamps to make them stick. Nancy _____ stamps all day long.

35. The children will finish their work before lunch. This is the work they

    _____ .

36. Toby parts his hair on the right. The barber _____ Toby's hair on the left after he washed it.

37. Jeremiah wanted to receive the award. This is the award he _____ .

38. Justin likes to tease his friends. He's _____ all of them at one time or another.

39. Each captain could pick her teammates. These three girls were _____ first.

40. Clyde chops down dead trees. On Saturday, he _____ down two trees in his yard.

41. The Morgans were going to move. They _____ to Washington D.C. last month.

42. Mrs. Roberts practices her music every day. She _____ playing the piano late last night.

I.E.P. Goal: The student will supply regular past tense verb forms based on the context of sentences with 90% or greater accuracy.

The first sentence in each numbered item below describes an event.   Fill in the blank of the second sentence using the correct past tense verb form.   *Hint:* You will have to change the spelling!   The first one is done for you.

1. Marcie drinks her milk.   Dan already __*drank*_____ his milk.

2. You can fall from a tree.   Yesterday, Harry _____ from a tree.

3. Eat all your dinner, LaToya.   She _____ it all.

4. It is easy to forget.   Lou completely _____ her class.

5. I will do what my coach says.   He _____ what his coach told him.

6. You have to blow into some musical instruments.   Jake _____ into his trumpet.

7. Tomorrow, bring your lunch to school.   Last week, I _____ my lunch three times.

8. I can go to the movie.   Last night, we _____ to the late movie.

9. Run for your health.   They all _____ in the race.

10. The carpenter builds houses.   Here is a house he _____.

11. Jerome can catch the ball.   He _____ five passes today.

12. You can choose whatever color you like.   She _____ purple.

13. We'll have to dig a hole first.   We _____ a big one.

14. The assignment was to write a story.   The students shared the stories they

_____.

15. I will try to find it.   Here is what I _____.

16. Don't give that to Janice.   Megan _____ her one last year.

17. I want to see for myself.   I can't believe what I _____.

I.E.P. Goal: The student will supply past tense forms of irregular verbs with 90% or greater accuracy.

The first sentence in each numbered item below describes an event.   Fill in the blank of the second sentence using the correct past tense verb form.   *Hint:* You will have to change the spelling!

18. The quarterback can throw a long pass.   He _____ the ball 80 yards.

19. I will sit under the tree.   There's the spot where I _____.

20. The pilot can fly the airplane.   He _____ the plane home.

21. I wear my hat on windy days.   I _____ it last Friday.

22. The students sell pizzas.   They _____ three dozen in one hour.

23. Let's swim in the pond.   We _____ there last week.

24. Can you think of his name?   I haven't _____ of it.

25. When water is very cold, it freezes.   It _____ quickly.

26. I know the answer.   She _____ I had studied.

27. She'll leave it on the table.   That's exactly where she _____ it.

28. Please sweep up the mess.   The kids _____ it up for me.

29. I want to meet your new friends.   I'm glad I _____ them.

30. He is happy today.   He _____ happy yesterday, too.

31. Grandpa wants to win the lottery.   He _____ $5 last week.

32. I want to buy a blouse.   This is the one I _____.

33. We like to hide in the cornfield.   This is where we _____.

34. I like to ride horses.   "Miss Sal" is the horse I _____.

35. I'll take mashed potatoes tonight.   I ate all I _____.

36. I hope I don't lose.   I was crushed when I _____.

I.E.P. Goal: The student will supply past tense forms of irregular verbs with 90% or greater accuracy.

Name _____

The first sentence in each numbered item below describes an event.   Fill in the blank of the second sentence using the correct past tense verb form.   *Hint:* You will have to change the spelling!

37. Mrs. Inez loves to teach.   I appreciate all she _____ me.

38. Children sure do grow fast.   He _____ four inches.

39. I like to sing in the shower.   This is the song I _____.

40. We had to tear the paper into shreds.   We have piles of paper that we

_____.

41. Hang the picture over the couch.   This is where the picture was _____.

42. I'll keep the diary for you.   It was her diary I _____.

43. I'll tell you a great story.   That was the best story I've ever _____.

44. We'll get wet in the storm.   We _____ drenched.

45. Please hold your head still.   She _____ her head still as long as she could.

46. The bread will rise in the heat.   We baked it after it _____.

47. Dad makes good lasagna.   Last night, he _____ two pans of it.

48. Barrett can draw cartoons.   Here are some that he _____.

49. We bite with our teeth.   This is the carrot I _____.

50. I feel very sick.   I told my doctor how I _____.

51. Jordan can sleep anywhere.   This is the room where he _____.

52. This brick is going to sink.   It _____ in five seconds.

53. The athlete likes to dive.   He _____ into the pool two times.

54. Don't shake the drink too much.   It exploded when the boys _____ it.

I.E.P. Goal: The student will supply past tense forms of irregular verbs with 90% or greater accuracy.

Concepts

Knowledge of basic concepts is the cornerstone of the human language system. Mastery of basic concepts and the interrelationships of words and the objects and ideas they represent, foster cross-categorical learning and rich, meaningful communication.

To be able to use concepts meaningfully, students must understand the attributes of objects, events, places, and people and have a variety of schemata available for classifying these objects. Students with language deficits often have developed inflexible schemata for identification and classification. Once an object is placed in a certain schema it is likely to remain there, because the student is unable to recognize other attributes of an object that would allow it to be placed in another grouping.

The tasks presented in this section will enable the student to discern as well as to describe the relationships between individuals, times, places, things, events, and situations. This practice will enable the student to develop more flexible and varied vocabularies and schemata for classifying these words. Skillful use of this section will help students function as better communicators both in and out of the classroom, as they build their internal networks of classifying and assimilating information.

Name _____

Name the place where you usually find these things. The first one is done for you.

1. frying pan, dishes, sink, stove, forks   _kitchen_____

2. bed, dresser, blanket, lamp, pillow   _____

3. desks, books, pencil sharpener, teacher   _____

4. Popsicles, ice cubes, ice cream, meat   _____

5. carts, cashiers, aisles, frozen food, fresh vegetables   _____

6. washing machine, dirty clothes, dryer, detergent _____

7. dresses, pants, sweaters, blouses, shoes   _____

8. pants, ties, jackets, shirts, shoes   _____

9. menus, booths, food server, salad bar, cash register   _____

10. monkeys, bears, giraffes, lions, elephants   _____

11. cows, pigs, chickens, barn, tractor   _____

12. office, principal, cafeteria, gym, classrooms   _____

13. candy, popcorn, darkness, big screen, tickets   _____

14. tables, trays, chairs, students, food   _____

15. department store, shoe store, food court, movie theater   _____

16. hose, ladder, siren, flashing lights, driver   _____

17. clowns, jugglers, trapeze, popcorn, acrobats   _____

18. bands, floats, clowns, fire engines   _____

19. toys, nap mats, small children, teachers, snacks _____

20. pilot, flight attendant, emergency exit, wings   _____

I.E.P. Goal: When presented with lists of common items, the student will identify the places the items are usually found with 90% or greater accuracy.

Name _____

Name the place where you usually find these things.

21. stamps, mailboxes, clerks, scales, envelopes   _____

22. water, ladder, steps, diving board, drain   _____

23. waves, sand, lifeguard, shells, crabs   _____

24. drill, mirror, toothbrush, dental floss, reclining chair   _____

25. balls, lanes, pins, shoes, gutter, snack bar   _____

26. curlers, shampoo, scissors, hair spray, sinks, customers   _____

27. doctors, patients, beds, medicine, nurses   _____

28. Ferris wheel, tickets, cotton candy, games, noise   _____

29. life jacket, oars, motor, fishing poles, bait   _____

30. helmets, goalposts, cheerleaders, players, fans   _____

31. gas tanks, oil cans, paper towels, cars, customers   _____

32. cacti, sand, heat, tumbleweed, snakes   _____

33. traffic, skyscrapers, crowds, taxis, bright lights   _____

34. steering wheel, seats, dashboard, glove compartment, radio   _____

35. fish, coral, shells, divers, treasure, plants   _____

36. trees, deer, moss, rabbits, shade, ferns   _____

37. pavement, guard rails, speed limit signs, state troopers   _____

38. candy, snacks, cold soda, magazines, counter, clerk   _____

39. money, checks, tellers, safe, guard   _____

40. watches, rings, bracelets, necklaces, alarm system   _____

I.E.P. Goal: When presented with lists of common items, the student will identify the places the items are usually found with 90% or greater accuracy.

Concepts   90

Name _____

Choose the correct answer for each question.   The first one is done for you.

1. Do you find pillows on the bed or under the bed?   (on)   under

2. Do you put water in a glass or on a glass?   in   on

3. Do you put bread on a toaster or in a toaster?   on   in

4. Do squirrels live inside or outside a building?   inside   outside

5. Does cheese go on or under a pizza?   on   under

6. Do you put keys in or on a lock?   in   on

7. When you eat, do you sit under or at a table?   under   at

8. Do you eat lunch in or on the cafeteria?   in   on

9. In a car, do passengers sit beside or below each other?   beside   below

10. Do you put money under a soda machine or in a soda machine?   under   in

11. Do you wear a hat on your head or over your head?   on   over

12. To ride a bike, do you get in or on the bike?   in   on

13. Do people dive on the water or in the water?   on   in

14. Do you look through or around a pair of glasses?   through   around

15. Do you look through a movie or at a movie?   through   at

16. Does the leader stand at the front or the back of the line?   front   back

17. If you are last in line, are you standing after or before your friends?   after   before

18. After lunch, do you go into or out of the cafeteria?   into   out of

19. When using a telephone, do you hold the receiver next to your ear or in between your ears?   next to   in between

20. Does mail go in or around the mailbox?   in   around

I.E.P. Goal: Given a choice of responses, the student will answer questions concerning spatial relationships with 90% or greater accuracy.

Name _____

21. Do you hang your coat on or off a hook?   on   off

22. To fill a cup with cocoa, do you pour the cocoa in or out of a pan?   in   out

23. Do dishes go below or on a table?   below   on

24. Should you step into or across a puddle?   into   across

25. Are the doors located in the front or on the side of a car?   in the front   on the side

26. Do you walk down or around a hallway?   down   around

27. In the shower, does the water run up or down your legs?   up   down

28. On Monday morning, do you go to or from school?   to   from

29. Should you lean up against or away from a hot stove?   up against   away from

30. Do you put your arm through or under your sleeve?   through   under

31. When you shake hands with someone, do you stand close to or away from them?   close to   away from

32. When sewing on a button, does the needle go beside or through the cloth?   beside   through

33. Should you walk in front of or away from a moving train?   in front of   away from

34. Are seeds found around or inside grapes?   around   inside

35. Does a horse jump over or between a log?   over   between

36. When you fold your hands, are your hands together or apart?   together   apart

37. Are the soles of your feet on the top or the bottom of your body?   top   bottom

38. Does the winner of a race cross the finish line next to or in front of the other racers?   next to   in front of

39. Do the laces on tennis shoes go across or around the shoes?   across   around

40. Are the yellow lines painted down or across a road?   down   across

I.E.P. Goal: *Given a choice of responses, the student will answer questions concerning spatial relationships with 90% or greater accuracy.*

Concepts   92

Name _____

Name the activity you would do using the items below.   The first one is done for you.

1. knife, apple   _slice an apple_____

2. candle, match   _____

3. axe, log   _____

4. camera, film   _____

5. snow, hat, scarf, carrot, two sticks   _____

6. stapler, staples, two pieces of paper   _____

7. airplane, parachute   _____

8. hill, snow, sled   _____

9. water, toothpaste, toothbrush, dental floss   _____

10. pajamas, pillow, bed, alarm clock   _____

11. hose, bucket, sponge, soap, car   _____

12. colorful paper, box, tape, scissors, bow   _____

13. peanut butter, honey, knife, bread   _____

14. hot water, shampoo, towel, comb   _____

15. dishes, detergent, hot water, sink, sponge   _____

16. scissors, paste, colored paper, crayons   _____

17. books, pencil, assignment, paper   _____

18. bat, ball, bases, pitcher, home plate   _____

19. rake, lawn mower, trash bag, clippers   _____

20. dishes, silverware, napkins, drinks, food   _____

I.E.P. Goal: The student will identify activities performed when using specific items with 90% or greater accuracy.

Concepts   93

 More **Lesson 3**

Name the activity you would do using the items below.

21. paint, brush, roller, ladder, rags   _____

22. lettuce, tomatoes, carrots, knife, bowl   _____

23. clean diapers, wet cloth, lotion, baby   _____

24. suitcase, tickets, camera, money, clothes   _____

25. dough, rolling pin, cookie cutters, oven   _____

26. charcoal, grill, hot dogs, buns, matches   _____

27. board, dice, play money, cards   _____

28. rackets, net, balls, players   _____

29. bucket, water, mop, soap   _____

30. vacuum cleaner, electrical outlet, carpet   _____

31. guests, soda, music, snacks, decorations   _____

32. knife, newspapers, pumpkin, spoon, candle   _____

33. thumbtacks, cardboard letters, students' work,
     roll of paper   _____

34. tent, sleeping bag, flashlight, bug spray, food _____

35. bait, hook, line, pole, knife   _____

36. blanket, saddle, stirrups, reins   _____

37. boiling water, pot, pasta, sauce   _____

38. old tire, rope, sturdy tree branch   _____

39. stage, curtain, actors, script, audience   _____

40. wood, saw, nails, hammer, sandpaper, drill   _____

I.E.P. Goal: The student will identify activities performed when using specific items with 90% or greater accuracy.

Concepts   94

Name _____

For each word on the left, choose the appropriate descriptive word or words on the right. The first one is done for you.

1. baby	(soft)	(young)	sharp
2. spoon	rough	shiny	hard
3. blanket	warm	slimy	soft
4. knife	salty	sharp	soft
5. building	big	tall	fuzzy
6. skunk	smelly	blue	large
7. elephant	tiny	big	gray
8. feather	light	heavy	sour
9. jelly	long	sweet	sticky
10. crayon	hot	colorful	pointed
11. ice cream	cold	warm	tired
12. fire	cool	bright	hot
13. road	long	smart	cute
14. roller coaster	scary	quiet	bumpy
15. popcorn	fluffy	salty	heavy
16. hair	curly	wavy	long
17. tiger	weak	wild	crooked
18. pine cone	rough	smooth	sharp
19. rainstorm	loud	sour	tough
20. police officer	helpful	green	salty

I.E.P. Goal: *When presented with groups of adjectives, the student will identify those which describe common items with 90% or greater accuracy.*

 **More** **Lesson 4**

Name _____

For each word on the left, choose the appropriate descriptive word or words on the right.

21. cave	cheerful	rich	dark
22. banana	mushy	happy	ripe
23. penny	square	silky	shiny
24. shoe	frizzy	dirty	scared
25. chalk	dusty	oily	round
26. clown	mean	funny	lively
27. slide	slippery	sleepy	unhappy
28. snake	furry	smooth	long
29. marble	hard	wrinkled	pretty
30. squirrel	huge	quick	slimy
31. orange	sweet	round	juicy
32. skin	smooth	wrinkled	soft
33. pretzel	salty	crunchy	tasty
34. whale	tiny	enormous	helpful
35. flower	heavy	pretty	fragrant
36. ballerina	jolly	clumsy	graceful
37. pizza	delicious	harmful	steady
38. book bag	fragile	sturdy	useful
39. movie	interesting	handy	exciting
40. fishbowl	ragged	breakable	transparent

I.E.P. Goal: When presented with groups of adjectives, the student will identify those which describe common items with 90% or greater accuracy.

Concepts   96

Tell at least three things about each item below.   Think about what it does, what it looks like, what parts it has, and what you do with it.   The first one is done for you.

1. teddy bear   (*soft, furry, toy*)   21. yo-yo

2. crayon   22. drum

3. flower   23. comb

4. slide   24. newspaper

5. marshmallow   25. ladder

6. bathtub   26. alarm clock

7. toothbrush   27. piano

8. television   28. pair of scissors

9. turkey   29. ruler

10. elephant   30. umbrella

11. zebra   31. tent

12. frog   32. roller skates

13. shoe   33. stove

14. jacket   34. hair dryer

15. fire truck   35. pair of glasses

16. pillow   36. barn

17. birthday cake   37. telephone book

18. merry-go-round   38. key

19. apple   39. calendar

20. rocking chair   40. dictionary

I.E.P. Goal: *When presented with items, the student will list their attributes, parts, or functions using three descriptors with 90% or greater accuracy.*

Concepts   97

 **Lesson 6**

Name _____

Answer *yes* or *no* to these questions.   The first one is done for you.

1. Can you pour syrup on ice cream?   (yes)   no

2. Do people live under a house?   yes   no

3. Do apples grow on a tree?   yes   no

4. Can you sit on top of yourself?   yes   no

5. Do you pour juice under a glass?   yes   no

6. Does a chair sit on the floor?   yes   no

7. Can you wear a bracelet on your wrist?   yes   no

8. Is the ceiling below your head?   yes   no

9. Can everyone be last in line?   yes   no

10. Can a dog jump through a hoop?   yes   no

11. Does a bird fly over the rooftops?   yes   no

12. Do people wear glasses under their noses?   yes   no

13. Does a baby chick grow inside its shell?   yes   no

14. Can a rubber band go around a newspaper?   yes   no

15. Does a collar go inside a dog's neck?   yes   no

16. Do the horses on a merry-go-round go around?   yes   no

17. Can a boy be taller than his brother?   yes   no

18. Can a baby be older than its grandmother?   yes   no

19. Is a caboose behind the rest of the cars on a train?   yes   no

20. If you stand up, is the floor beneath you?   yes   no

I.E.P. Goal: When presented with relational questions containing one variable, the student will answer yes *or* no
        with 90% or greater accuracy.

Concepts   98

Answer *yes* or *no* to these questions.

21. Can you look around a window?   yes   no

22. If you take a bath, is the water around you?   yes   no

23. When you swallow, does the food go down your throat?   yes   no

24. Do you screw a light bulb beside the socket?   yes   no

25. Do you kick a football over the goalpost?   yes   no

26. Are your ears above your shoulders?   yes   no

27. Are your feet beside your knees?   yes   no

28. Is an eraser inside a pencil?   yes   no

29. Does a staple go through the paper?   yes   no

30. Are your eyelids over your eyes?   yes   no

31. Can a truck pass through a tunnel?   yes   no

32. Can you sit between a chair?   yes   no

33. Are your ears behind your head?   yes   no

34. Do you spread peanut butter through crackers?   yes   no

35. Do your fingernails grow around your fingers?   yes   no

36. Is a pillow placed inside a pillowcase?   yes   no

37. Do you throw a coin over a wishing well?   yes   no

38. Do the roots of a plant lie above the soil?   yes   no

39. Can you walk under an arch?   yes   no

40. Is the core found inside an apple?   yes   no

I.E.P. Goal: When presented with relational questions containing one variable, the student will answer yes or no with 90% or greater accuracy.

Concepts   99

Name _____

Choose the correct answer to each question.   The first one is done for you.

1. Do you eat dinner before or after you go to bed?   (before)   after

2. Do you go to school before or after you get dressed?   before   after

3. Do little children go to bed before or after midnight?   before   after

4. When you get dressed, do you put on your jacket first or last?   first   last

5. At dinner, does dessert come first or last?   first   last

6. Do children go to first grade before or after kindergarten?   before   after

7. Do we come home from school in the morning or afternoon?   morning   afternoon

8. Does it get dark at the middle or the end of the day?   middle   end

9. When you see a show, do you clap at the beginning or the end?   beginning   end

10. When you visit someone, do you wipe your feet before or after you walk in the front door?   before   after

11. Do you eat lunch at the middle or the end of the day?   middle   end

12. Does the sun rise at the beginning or the end of the day?   beginning   end

13. Does noon come before or after three o'clock in the afternoon?   before   after

14. Does eight o'clock in the morning come before or after one o'clock in the afternoon?   before   after

15. If the telephone rings, should you answer it while it is ringing or after it stops ringing?   while it is ringing   after it stops

I.E.P. Goal: Given a choice of two responses, the student will answer questions concerning temporal relationships with 90% or greater accuracy.

Concepts

Choose the correct answer to each question.

16. If you see a fire, should you call the fire station right now or later on?   right now   later on

17. Does Wednesday come before or after Friday?   before   after

18. If today is Sunday, is Monday tomorrow or yesterday?   tomorrow   yesterday

19. If today is Wednesday, is Tuesday tomorrow or yesterday?   tomorrow   yesterday

20. If this is June, is July next month or last month?   next month   last month

21. If this is January, is February next month or last month?   next month   last month

22. If this is August, is summer now or later?   now   later

23. If this is December, is spring now or later?   now   later

24. Is the end of a story during the first or last part of a book?   first part   last part

25. When riding in a boat, should you take off your life jacket during or after the ride?   during   after

26. If someone asks you a question, should you answer him while he asks the question or after he asks the question?   while   after

27. At a movie, are the lights out before or during the show?   before   during

28. If your mother asks you to do your chores right away, should you do them in the next hour or the next day?   hour   day

29. If your grandfather tells you he is coming to visit soon, will you see him in one week or one year?   one week   one year

30. If your teacher wants to see you immediately, should you go to his room right now or tomorrow?   right now   tomorrow

I.E.P. Goal: Given a choice of two responses, the student will answer questions concerning temporal relationships with 90% or greater accuracy.

Name _____

Choose the correct answer for each question.   The first one is done for you.

1. Which is more scary, feeding a kitten or feeding a tiger?

    kitten   (tiger)

2. Which is heavier, a chair or a cup?

    chair   cup

3. Which is more dangerous, playing soccer or fighting a fire?

    soccer   fire

4. Which is more fun, going to the doctor's office or going on a picnic?

    doctor's office   picnic

5. Which is a nicer present, a new game or a slice of bread?

    new game   slice of bread

6. Which is quicker, pouring a glass of water or making a milk shake?

    water   milk shake

7. Which takes less time, washing your hands or taking a bath?

    washing your hands   taking a bath

8. Which costs more, a granola bar or a pair of shoes?

    granola bar   pair of shoes

9. Which is better for you, a piece of cake or an apple?

    cake   apple

10. Which is easier to peel, a banana or an orange?

    banana   orange

I.E.P. Goal: The student will answer questions comparing situations or events with 90% or greater accuracy.

Choose the correct answer for each question.

11. Which takes more people to do, play kick ball or play the piano?

   play kick ball   play the piano

12. Which breaks more easily if you drop it, a basket or a mirror?

   basket   mirror

13. Which is harder to do, color a picture or multiply numbers?

   color a picture   multiply numbers

14. Which is longer, a morning or a day?

   morning   day

15. Which costs less, a bicycle or a lunch box?

   bicycle   lunch box

16. Which should you do first after dinner, do your homework or play games?

   do your homework   play games

17. Which tastes better, flour or sugar?

   flour   sugar

18. For which task do you need to be stronger, pushing a baby carriage or a lawn mower?

   baby carriage   lawn mower

19. Which takes more work, building a model ship or taking out the garbage?

   building a model ship   taking out the garbage

20. Which one makes you happier, washing the dishes or going swimming?

   washing dishes   going swimming

I.E.P. Goal: The student will answer questions comparing situations or events with 90% or greater accuracy.

Name _____

Choose the correct answer for each question.

21. Which makes more noise, a frog or a dog?

               frog   dog

22. Which is more popular, playing a video game or playing marbles?

           video game   marbles

23. Which is more thrilling, climbing a mountain or going for a walk?

        climbing a mountain   going for a walk

24. Which takes more planning, going to the movies or getting a snack from the refrigerator?

        going to the movies   getting a snack

25. Which would make you feel prouder, getting a good grade on your report card or finding a piece of gum in your pocket?

        getting a good grade   finding some gum

26. Which is more likely to be crowded, a school at midnight or a grocery store at noon?

        school at midnight   store at noon

27. Which takes more energy, riding in an elevator or roller skating?

        riding in an elevator   roller skating

28. Which can jump higher, a kangaroo or a rabbit?

         kangaroo   rabbit

29. Which is more of a risk, eating soup with a fork or riding a bicycle without a helmet?

         eating soup   riding a bike

30. Who is more easily seen outside at night, someone wearing a white shirt or someone wearing a black jacket?

         white shirt   black jacket

I.E.P. Goal: *The student will answer questions comparing situations or events with 90% or greater accuracy.*

Social Language

Social language skills involve using language as a tool to communicate with others. Children with weak social language skills may communicate inadequately because they are unable to initiate a conversation, keep it going, or explain their views and opinions easily. They may not be able to determine what information is pertinent and what is irrelevant and, as a result, may withdraw from communicating.

The goal of social language training is to help students develop functional, practical language skills that will transfer to their everyday environment. The tasks in this section offer a broad base for developing social language skills. Conversational practice in a variety of realistic settings will help students develop and refine their social language skills in natural contexts.

Use your own judgment in presenting the tasks as oral or written exercises. Since conversation has few "right" or "wrong" responses, accept reasonable responses as correct. Answers are provided in the Answer Key only for tasks with fairly predictable responses.

Pretend you did each activity below and you want to tell someone about it. Tell how it made you feel, who was there, what you heard, smelled, felt, or saw, or anything else that you would want the other person to know. The first one is done for you.

1. cleaning up your room when it was very messy
   (*It took me all day. My mom said I had to do it. I hung up all my clothes.*)

2. eating pizza in a restaurant

3. going to visit your grandparents

4. buying a new pair of shoes

5. going to the grocery store with your mom or dad

6. being late for school

7. playing hide-and-seek

8. giving a dog a bath

9. walking home from school in the rain

10. riding the bus downtown

11. sliding down a hill in the snow

12. going on a picnic in the summer

13. watching a parade pass by

14. raking up fall leaves and jumping in them

15. going on a field trip to the zoo

16. checking out a book from the library

17. getting a haircut

18. going on a long trip with your family

19. winning an award for an art project

20. building a play fort in the backyard

21. losing your first tooth

22. falling off a swing and skinning your knee

23. playing pin the tail on the donkey

24. pretending you're a superhero

25. spending the night away from home for the first time

26. getting lost in the mall

27. thinking there's a monster under your bed

28. learning how to ride a bike

29. flying a kite on a windy day

30. making a bowl out of clay

31. babysitting for a younger child

32. going to a slumber party

33. playing miniature golf with your friends

34. acting in a school play

35. getting stuck at the top of the Ferris wheel

I.E.P. Goal: The student will describe common events, providing at least three (four, five) different descriptors with 90% or greater accuracy.

Name _____

Choose the polite response for each situation below.   The first one is done for you.

1. If your neighbor says "Good morning," you say:

   (a.) Hello.
   b. nothing

2. If you want more toast, you say:

   a. More toast, now!
   b. I'd like more toast, please.

3. If someone calls for your sister and she's not home, you say:

   a. Wrong number.
   b. Please call back later.

4. When someone says "How are you today?", you say:

   a. Fine, thanks.
   b. I don't know.

5. If your friend's mother asks if you want to stay for dinner, you say:

   a. Thank you for asking, but I can't.
   b. No, my mom's a much better cook.

6. If your dad makes soup that you don't like, you say:

   a. This is yucky and I'm not eating it.
   b. I tasted the soup, but I don't like it.

7. If you need to borrow a pencil in class, you say:

   a. May I borrow your pencil?
   b. Give me your pencil.

8. If the librarian asks you to be quiet, you say:

   a. Make me.
   b. Okay, I'll try to whisper.

9. If your sister asks to borrow your new paints, you say:

   a. No, but you may use my old paints.
   b. Not in a million years!

10. If your teacher asks for a volunteer to take something to the office, you say:

    a. How much will you pay?
    b. I'd like to go.

11. If your father asks if you've finished your chores, you say:

    a. I'm sorry.   I haven't had time to do them.
    b. Quit bugging me!   I'll get them done.

12. If your grandfather starts to tell you a story you've heard before, you say:

    a. Oh yeah, I remember this story.
    b. Oh no, not this old story again.

13. If you break your mother's watch, you say:

    a. It's not my fault.   It's a stupid watch anyway.
    b. I'm sorry I broke it.   It was an accident.

14. If your friend asks if you like her new bike, you say:

    a. I like mine better.
    b. Yes, it's a great-looking bike.

I.E.P. Goal: The student will choose the polite responses to use in given situations with 90% or greater accuracy.

Choose the polite response for each situation below.

15. If your aunt gives you a birthday gift you don't like, you say:

   a. It's not what I asked for.

   b. Thank you for the gift.

16. When you accidently bump into someone, you say:

   a. Excuse me.

   b. Watch where you're going!

17. If someone cuts in front of you in line, you say:

   a. Hey, move it!

   b. The line ends back there.

18. If someone behind you in the movies is talking too loudly, you say:

   a. Pipe down!

   b. Please be quiet.   I can't hear the movie.

19. If a friend asks to copy your homework, you say:

   a. I'd rather not share my homework.

   b. I'm going to tell on you!

20. If the waiter brings you the wrong sandwich, you say:

   a. This isn't the sandwich I ordered.

   b. I hate grilled cheese.   Take it back.

21. If your little sister comes to you with a broken doll, you say:

   a. You always break everything.

   b. Let's see if we can fix it.

22. If you are trying to find notebook paper at the store, you say:

   a. Mister, where are you hiding the notebook paper?

   b. Excuse me.   Where is the notebook paper?

23. If your teacher grades your paper incorrectly, you say:

   a. Will you please check this again?

   b. You didn't check your work.

24. If a friend says something bad about another friend, you say:

   a. You liar!

   b. I'd rather not talk about Carl behind his back.

25. When you see your best friend after you've had an argument, you say:

   a. Not you again!

   b. I'm sorry we argued.

26. If your teacher asks you if your parents will be home this evening, you say:

   a. Yes, I think my dad will be at home.

   b. Why do you want to know?

27. While going for a walk with friends, a woman asks if you've seen her cat. You say:

   a. Not me – I don't even like cats.

   b. No, I haven't, but I hope you find it.

I.E.P. Goal: The student will choose the polite responses to use in given situations with 90% or greater accuracy.

 **Lesson 3**

Name _____

For each situation below, tell what you would say to start a conversation with someone. The first one is done for you.

1. A new child moves next door to you.   (*Where did you used to live?*)

2. You call your aunt on her birthday.

3. Your best friend comes home from a long trip.

4. Your dad comes home from work early.

5. Your mother picks you up at school.

6. Your friends are playing ball and you want to join them.

7. The girl in front of you in line at the cafeteria drops her ticket.

8. You're coloring a picture in class and you don't have a red crayon.

9. You see your neighbor walking down the street with a new dog.

10. A classmate comes to school wearing a cast on his arm.

11. Your sister is sitting by herself looking sad.

12. Your little cousin is about to put a rock in his mouth.

13. You need help finding a book in the library.

14. You see a little boy crying on the playground.

15. Your grandfather comes to your house carrying a big package.

16. You see your music teacher in the grocery store.

17. A new girl sits beside you on the school bus.

18. You see a child looking under your car.

19. A little boy is skating in the wrong direction at the roller rink.

20. You leave your teacher on the last day of school.

I.E.P. Goal: When presented with various situations, the student will give appropriate sentences to begin conversations with 90% or greater accuracy.

Name _____

For each situation below, tell what you would say to start a conversation with someone.

21. Your friend invites you to his birthday party.

22. A girl in your class is wearing a sweater just like yours.

23. Your grandmother drives up in a new car.

24. Your little sister wakes up crying in the middle of the night.

25. A man gets out of his car and leaves the lights on.

26. Your uncle is wearing a purple tie with green frogs on it.

27. Your best friend won't talk to you.

28. Your classmate missed three days of school.

29. You notice your neighbor getting his ladder out of the garage.

30. You want to order something at the ice-cream store.

31. You see a clown at a parade giving out balloons.

32. You're on the bus and your bus driver drives past your bus stop.

33. You notice someone's shoe is untied.

34. Your mother makes a special meal for you.

35. You want to order lunch at a fast-food restaurant.

36. You ripped a friend's book when you borrowed it.

37. Your friend comes to your house wearing new roller skates.

38. You call your mom at work and a stranger answers.

39. Your sister comes home after her team lost the football game.

40. The person behind you at a baseball game asks his friend the score but his friend doesn't know.

I.E.P. Goal: When presented with various situations, the student will give appropriate sentences to begin conversations with 90% or greater accuracy.

Name _____

Each item below starts a conversation.   Think of a question or sentence that would keep the conversation going.   The first one is done for you.

1. My favorite thing on the playground is the slide.   (*Why is it your favorite?*)

2. Kickball is more fun than softball.

3. If I could have any food I wanted, I'd pick popcorn.

4. I can't find my lunch money.

5. I like to help my brother make dinner.

6. My baby sister eats with her hands.

7. My favorite color is purple.

8. It was so cold last night I couldn't sleep.

9. I think children should be able to watch TV every night until midnight.

10. Fourth grade is the best one of all.

11. My best friend is moving away next week.

12. My mom said we might go to the circus.

13. We went to the neatest toy store yesterday.

14. Sarah has a new baby sister.

15. My brother is in the school's marching band.

16. I remember when I broke my toe and was on crutches for two weeks.

17. I wish I didn't have to make my bed every morning.

18. My dad likes to put ketchup on his eggs.

19. It must be fun to have a lot of brothers and sisters.

20. I'm taking care of my neighbors' dog while they're away.

I.E.P. Goal: When presented with questions or statements that begin conversations, the student will provide statements or questions maintaining each topic with 90% or greater accuracy.

Each item below starts a conversation.   Think of a question or sentence that would keep the conversation going.

21. I'm saving my money to buy a raft.

22. Do you like to collect anything?

23. I hope I get a new soccer ball for my birthday.

24. I love going to my grandma's and playing in her attic.

25. I'm going to be in my uncle's wedding.

26. Yesterday there was a fire truck in front of the school.

27. I can hold my breath for five minutes.

28. My cousin's hair is so long she can sit on it.

29. I wonder where bumblebees go in the winter.

30. My brother is so tall he has to duck his head when he walks through the door.

31. I wish I was the oldest child in the family.

32. You should always wear a seat belt in the car.

33. I love to catch fireflies at night.

34. It rains every Saturday morning.

35. I wonder what it's like to be 100 years old.

36. What would we do without telephones?

37. Summer is my favorite season.

38. I had the best time ever when I went to a major league football game.

39. I remember when I was so little I couldn't reach the sink to wash my hands.

40. I wonder if astronauts take baths in outer space.

I.E.P. Goal: When presented with questions or statements that begin conversations, the student will provide statements or questions maintaining each topic with 90% or greater accuracy.

 **Lesson 5**

Name _____

For each situation below, give the last sentence or two to finish the conversation.   The first one is done for you.

1. Your teacher says, "Where's your homework?"   What would you say?

    (*It's in my notebook.   I'll get it.*)

2. Your mother says, "Do you want oatmeal or eggs for breakfast?"   What would you say?

3. Your friend says, "I like your new shoes."   What would you say?

4. When you come to school in the morning, the principal says, "Nice to see you today."
    What would you say?

5. When you come downstairs for breakfast, your mother says, "I like the way you have
    combed your hair."   What would you say?

6. Your grandmother has just given you a present.   She says, "I wrapped it in your favorite
    color of paper."   What would you say?

7. You buy some pencils at the school store.   The person behind the counter says, "Do you
    need anything else?"   What would you say?

8. Your best friend is going home after spending the night at your house.   He says, "Thanks
    for having me stay over."   What would you say?

9. You ask your mother if you can have some ice cream.   She says, "Not now.   We're going
    to eat dinner soon."   What would you say?

10. Your sister says, "You borrowed my favorite pen and didn't give it back."   What would you say?

11. Your brother says, "Tomorrow, I'm going to a movie."   What would you say?

12. A boy in your class is having a birthday.   He says, "Can you come to my party next
    Saturday?"   What would you say?

13. The girl sitting next to you in class says, "What pages are we supposed to read?"
    What would you say?

14. Your neighbor says, "Ask your mother if she wants some tomatoes from our garden."
    What would you say?

15. A clerk in the shoe store says, "How do these shoes feel?"   What would you say?

I.E.P. Goal: *The student will provide the sentences to terminate conversations appropriately with 90% or greater*
       accuracy.

For each situation below, give the last sentence or two to finish the conversation.

16. Your aunt says, "Did you have a good time on your vacation?"   What would you say?

17. The doctor says, "You need to get plenty of rest and drink lots of juice."   What would you say?

18. A clerk in the pet store says, "Can I help you?"   What would you say?

19. Your grandfather calls and tells you he misses you.   He says, "I wish you would write to me sometime."   What would you say?

20. A stranger calls on the telephone and says, "Hello.   Can I speak to Dagwood Dumpster?" What would you say?

21. Your coach says, "We missed you at practice last week."   What would you say?

22. A friend has returned your book with the cover stained.   She says, "My brother spilled hot chocolate on it."   What would you say?

23. At the movies, a boy sitting behind you says, "Will you move over one seat so I can see better?"   What would you say?

24. The school bus driver says, "When you get off the bus, be careful.   There's a lot of traffic today."   What would you say?

25. A girl in the library says, "I need to use the telephone.   Do you have change for a dollar?" What would you say?

26. You accidently ripped your sister's art project.   Your sister says, "It's due tomorrow and now it is ruined!"   What would you say?

27. Your best friend has just found out she's moving far away.   She says, "I don't want to go. I know I'm not going to like it there."   What would you say?

28. A boy in your class just won first prize in an essay contest.   He says, "I can't believe I won!" What would you say?

29. Your music teacher says, "I can tell you haven't practiced this lesson."   What would you say?

30. Your teacher says, "I'd like you to play the lead in the school play."   What would you say?

I.E.P. Goal: The student will provide the sentences to terminate conversations appropriately with 90% or greater accuracy.

Name _____

Tell why you couldn't do each thing below.   The first one is done for you.

Why couldn't you...

1. build a snowman in the summertime? (*There's no snow in the summer.*)

2. keep your bicycle under your bed?

3. ride a train across the ocean?

4. play hide-and-seek by yourself?

5. comb your hair with a spoon?

6. park the car in the house?

7. brush your teeth with a hairbrush?

8. take a bath in the sink?

9. cut firewood with scissors?

10. ride a bike without wheels?

11. play tennis without a racket?

12. jump rope in a closet?

13. use a balloon to play baseball?

14. make ice cream in the microwave oven?

15. use a ruler to weigh yourself?

16. use a rabbit as a watchdog?

17. keep your pet turtle in the refrigerator?

18. go ice skating on the pond in July?

19. make lemonade with oranges?

20. make an apple pie with potatoes?

21. ride the city bus without paying for a ticket?

22. carry water in a sock?

23. take your socks off before your shoes?

24. play Ping-Pong with a bowling ball?

25. look in the refrigerator without opening the door?

26. eat a sandwich underwater?

27. wear glasses if you had no ears?

28. paint a picture of green grass if you only have blue and orange paint?

29. put out a fire with gasoline?

30. sing without opening your mouth?

31. ride in an elevator if the power went off?

32. walk up the stairs without bending your knees?

33. play checkers using only the red checkers?

34. make peanuts from peanut butter?

35. divide a dollar evenly among three children?

36. change your birth date to a different date?

I.E.P. Goal: The student will tell why situations could not occur with 90% or greater accuracy.

Social Language   115

Tell why you shouldn't do each thing below.   The first one is done for you.

Why shouldn't you . . .

1. give the baby scissors to play with?
   (*He might hurt himself.*)

2. wear your best clothes on the playground?

3. leave your bicycle in the driveway?

4. rub your eyes if your hands are soapy?

5. cross the street with your eyes closed?

6. go swimming while wearing boots?

7. leave your flashlight on all night?

8. put a letter in the mailbox without a stamp?

9. put your paint brush away without washing it?

10. walk down the stairs at night without turning on the light?

11. brush your teeth with your sister's toothbrush?

12. drink grape juice while sitting on the couch?

13. play in the sandbox during a rainstorm?

14. go for a walk around the block in bare feet?

15. use only hot water when taking a shower?

16. open your neighbor's door without knocking first?

17. talk out loud during a movie?

18. put the eggs on the bottom of the grocery cart?

19. put your pen in the pencil sharpener?

20. swim in the ocean by yourself?

21. call a friend after 9:30 at night?

22. wash the toaster in the sink?

23. plant a garden in the winter?

24. eat food while in a clothing store?

25. wear new boots while marching in a parade?

26. order a pizza if you don't have any money?

27. put a plastic bowl on a hot stove?

28. play cards without shuffling them?

29. eat hot soup right out of the pot?

30. leave your dog in the car with all the windows rolled up in the summer?

31. run around if your clothing catches on fire?

32. give your library book to your friend for his birthday?

33. yell at a basketball player who is trying to make a free shot?

34. wear track shoes when bowling?

35. walk on the right-hand side of the road?

I.E.P. Goal: The student will tell why situations should not occur with 90% or greater accuracy.

Name _____

Use a sentence to tell why each statement isn't true.   The first one is done for you.

1. All dogs have long ears.   (*Terriers have short ears.*)

2. All cars have four doors.

3. If you cut a doll's hair, it will grow back.

4. Brothers and sisters never fight with each other.

5. Leaves fall off the trees in the summer.

6. Tigers make good pets.

7. Everyone in the first grade is six years old.

8. Babies don't learn to walk until they are two years old.

9. Some snakes have legs.

10. If you put water in the freezer, it will turn into ice cream.

11. Bananas are the only fruit that is yellow.

12. If you spill ketchup on your shirt, you should throw it away.

13. Everyone has a middle name.

14. Vegetables should not be eaten raw.

15. Teachers must be women.

16. Your birthday is always on a Friday.

17. There are the same number of boys and girls in each class in our school.

18. Deer are the only animals with antlers.

19. The tallest child in every grade is the oldest.

20. February always has 28 days.

I.E.P. Goal: When presented with false statements, the student will deny the statements by presenting counter examples with 90% or greater accuracy.

Social Language   117

Defining and Describing

Defining and describing are skills we use to identify and classify objects, events, actions, and ideas. These two skills help us to perceive and understand our complex world. Consequently, children with weak descriptive skills, who define terms only in the narrowest sense, are limited in their abilities to use language to control their environments. By providing opportunities to define and describe objects by various criteria, you can help your students develop useful strategies which will enable them to communicate more effectively.

This unit provides numerous activities in which common concepts, objects, and actions are explored in various defining, describing, discriminating, and identifying tasks. The goal of this unit is to show students different ways of perceiving and communicating about their environment.

 Lesson 1

Name _____

Tell what we do with each thing or what it is for.   The first one is done for you.

1. A couch is for _*sitting on*_____.

2. Milk is for _____.

3. A slide is for _____.

4. Jump ropes are for _____.

5. A pencil is for _____.

6. A knife is for _____.

7. A telephone is for _____.

8. A snack is for _____.

9. We use an ear to _____.

10. Footballs are for _____.

11. A bathtub is for _____.

12. We use shampoo to _____.

13. Slippers are for _____.

14. We have eyes to _____.

15. A guitar is for _____.

16. A rake is used to _____.

17. Ice is used to _____.

18. A book is for _____.

19. Tissues are used to _____.

20. A song is for _____.

I.E.P. Goal: The student will identify functions of common items with 90% or greater accuracy.

Defining and Describing   119

Name _____

Tell what we do with each thing or what it is for.

21. Pajamas are for _____.

22. We use an airplane to _____.

23. A vacuum cleaner is used for _____.

24. Soap is used for _____.

25. A closet is used for _____.

26. We use sheets to _____.

27. Televisions are used for _____.

28. Shirts are for _____.

29. An umbrella is used to _____.

30. We use a table for _____.

31. We use a ladder to _____.

32. We use towels to _____.

33. Medicine is for _____.

34. Presents are for _____.

35. A motorcycle is for _____.

36. Money is for _____.

37. Flashlights are for _____.

38. A refrigerator is for _____.

39. Stairs are for _____.

40. We need directions to _____.

I.E.P. Goal: The student will identify functions of common items with 90% or greater accuracy.

Defining and Describing   120

 **Lesson 2**

Name _____

Tell when we use each thing. The first one is done for you.

1. We wear pajamas when _*we go to bed*_____.

2. We use a toothbrush when _____.

3. A chalkboard is used when _____.

4. We eat cereal when _____.

5. We answer the phone when _____.

6. We use a bathrobe when _____.

7. Coats are worn when _____.

8. I ride a bus when _____.

9. We take a shower when _____.

10. Children take naps when _____.

11. We wear shorts when _____.

12. We need a clock when _____.

13. We need a pencil sharpener when _____.

14. We see teachers when _____.

15. We drink water when _____.

16. We use paper towels when _____.

17. We call the fire department when _____.

18. We go to the library when _____.

19. We need a mailbox when _____.

20. We go to the bus stop when _____.

I.E.P. Goal: The student will identify the times or events when common items are used with 90% or greater accuracy.

Defining and Describing   121

Name _____

Tell when we use each thing.

21. We rake leaves when _____.

22. We fly kites when _____.

23. You need a spoon when _____.

24. We see a doctor when _____.

25. We hang up our clothes when _____.

26. We buy a movie ticket when _____.

27. People love to eat popcorn when _____.

28. We wash our clothes when _____.

29. You need scissors when _____.

30. People ride in an ambulance when _____.

31. You go sledding when _____.

32. You need a light bulb when _____.

33. We use a stapler when _____.

34. You use a VCR when _____.

35. A farmer uses a tractor when _____.

36. You need a racket when _____.

37. You need an oar when _____.

38. We play musical instruments when _____.

39. My mom writes checks when _____.

40. We call a mechanic when _____.

I.E.P. Goal: **The student will identify the times or events when common items are used with 90% or greater accuracy.**

Defining and Describing

 **Lesson 3**

Name _____

Tell what each thing looks like, feels like, smells like, sounds like, or tastes like. The first one is done for you.

1. Ice feels _*cold*_____.

2. A beach ball is _____.

3. Tape feels _____.

4. A jump rope looks _____.

5. A tissue feels _____.

6. A rock feels _____.

7. The bakery smells _____.

8. A wooden block feels _____.

9. A toy drum is _____.

10. An elephant looks _____.

11. Ice cream tastes _____.

12. A feather is _____.

13. A fire feels _____.

14. A crying baby looks _____.

15. Potato chips taste _____.

16. A Popsicle feels _____.

17. The monster looked _____.

18. The sidewalk felt _____.

19. The jumbo jet looks _____.

20. The painting looks _____.

I.E.P. Goal: The student will identify attributes of common items with 90% or greater accuracy.

Defining and Describing

Name _____

Tell what each thing looks like, feels like, smells like, sounds like, or tastes like.

21. The cup of soup felt _____.

22. Sugar tastes _____.

23. The trumpet was _____.

24. A pine cone feels _____.

25. The pancake looks _____.

26. The grass looks _____.

27. The water in the lake felt _____.

28. The man's beard felt _____.

29. The roses smelled _____.

30. The mirror was _____.

31. The skunk was _____.

32. The thunderclap was _____.

33. Syrup tastes _____.

34. A washcloth feels _____.

35. The apples taste _____.

36. In the library, it is _____.

37. A clown looks _____.

38. Peanuts are _____.

39. A space shuttle blasting off is _____.

40. Sandpaper feels _____.

I.E.P. Goal: The student will identify attributes of common items with 90% or greater accuracy.

Name _____

Tell what each thing looks like, feels like, smells like, sounds like, or tastes like.

41. The fire truck's siren was _____.

42. Pickles taste _____.

43. A mud puddle looks _____.

44. Cotton balls feel _____.

45. The bark of a tree is _____.

46. The music from the harp was _____.

47. The silk gown felt _____.

48. The spoiled milk smelled _____.

49. The bench felt _____.

50. Mabel's husband looks _____.

51. The giraffe's neck looked _____.

52. The sixteen-floor office building looked _____.

53. The dog's growl was _____.

54. The chalkboard looked _____.

55. The view from the mountaintop was _____.

56. The clouds look _____.

57. A raisin looks _____.

58. The newborn baby was _____.

59. The cologne smelled _____.

60. The man's winter coat feels _____.

I.E.P. Goal: The student will identify attributes of common items with 90% or greater accuracy.

Defining and Describing   125

Lesson 4

Name _____

Tell what group each thing belongs in.   The first one is done for you.

1. Dogs are *animals* .

2. Orange juice is a _____.

3. Ice cream is a _____.

4. Red is a _____.

5. An apple is a _____.

6. A foot is a _____.

7. A coat is a piece of _____.

8. Green beans are _____.

9. Saturday is a _____.

10. Roosters are _____.

11. Strawberries are _____.

12. A canary is a _____.

13. Popcorn is a _____.

14. A car is a _____.

15. Water is a _____.

16. A guitar is an _____.

17. Bees are _____.

18. A table is a piece of _____.

19. Soccer is a _____.

20. Cows are _____.

I.E.P. Goal: The student will identify the classes of common items with 90% or greater accuracy.

Defining and Describing   126

Name _____

Tell what group each thing belongs in.

21. A sweater is a piece of _____.

22. Your stomach is a _____.

23. A circle is a _____.

24. Daffodils are _____.

25. An uncle is a _____.

26. A carrot is a _____.

27. A bracelet is a piece of _____.

28. A sand bucket and shovel are _____.

29. Roast beef is a type of _____.

30. Gorillas are _____.

31. A tuba is a _____.

32. A bookshelf is a piece of _____.

33. A porcupine is an _____.

34. Rain is a type of _____.

35. Measles is an _____.

36. Summer is one of the _____.

37. A screwdriver is a _____.

38. An ambulance is a _____.

39. A fork is a _____.

40. A washing machine is an _____.

I.E.P. Goal: The student will identify the classes of common items with 90% or greater accuracy.

Defining and Describing   127

Name _____

Tell what each thing does.   The first one is done for you.

1. A bird _*flies*_____.

2. A stove _____.

3. A child _____.

4. A pen _____.

5. Teachers _____.

6. A crayon _____.

7. Detergent _____.

8. Teeth _____.

9. Marbles _____.

10. Scissors _____.

11. A zipper _____.

12. Ears _____.

13. A belt _____.

14. Shoelaces _____.

15. Leaves _____.

16. Tape _____.

17. Noses _____.

18. Lawn mowers _____.

19. A kite _____.

20. A dog _____.

21. Snow _____.

22. Doors _____.

23. A worm _____.

24. A diver _____.

25. A shovel _____.

26. A horse _____.

27. A bow and arrow _____.

28. Dolphins _____.

29. A tractor _____.

30. A bell _____.

31. Popcorn _____.

32. A cake _____.

33. Chickens _____.

34. A toy top _____.

35. A flower _____.

36. A hammer _____.

37. Rain _____.

38. Ice _____.

39. Plants _____.

40. Ducks _____.

*I.E.P. Goal: **The student will describe common items by naming the actions they perform with 90% or greater accuracy.***

Name _____

Tell what each thing does.

41. A fire _____.

42. An eye _____.

43. The wind _____.

44. Earmuffs _____.

45. A watch _____.

46. A baseball bat _____.

47. Windows _____.

48. A hand _____.

49. A blanket _____.

50. A canary _____.

51. Kangaroos _____.

52. Hearts _____.

53. Axes _____.

54. Spoons _____.

55. An eraser _____.

56. A student _____.

57. A skinned knee _____.

58. Eggs _____.

59. An air conditioner _____.

60. A doctor _____.

61. A mask _____.

62. The moon _____.

63. Toasters _____.

64. A VCR _____.

65. Blenders _____.

66. Calculators _____.

67. Mail carriers _____.

68. Thermometers _____.

69. Water _____.

70. A rooster _____.

71. Tourists _____.

72. An anchor _____.

73. Artists _____.

74. A raft _____.

75. A rubber band _____.

76. Sugar _____.

77. Mirrors _____.

78. Tablecloths _____.

79. A splinter _____.

80. An oar _____.

I.E.P. Goal: *The student will describe common items by naming the actions they perform with 90% or greater accuracy.*

Defining and Describing   129

 **Lesson 6**

Tell as many words as possible that could describe each item.   The first one is done for you.

1. cat   (*soft, furry, black, little*)

2. car

3. bush

4. block

5. pie

6. crayon

7. hat

8. milk

9. peanut butter

10. bowl

11. flower

12. scissors

13. Popsicle

14. sandwich

15. toothpaste

16. coloring book

17. shirt

18. clock

19. ladybug

20. drum

21. skunk

22. pajamas

23. television

24. grass

25. school bus

26. toaster

27. tennis ball

28. ice-cream cone

29. stick

30. egg

31. strawberry

32. grandmother

33. sand

34. popcorn

35. bear

36. roller skate

37. lamp

38. hot dog

39. saw

40. kite

I.E.P. Goal: The student will generate adjectives to describe common nouns with 90% or greater accuracy.

Name _____

Tell as many words as possible that could describe each item.

41. watch

42. fishing pole

43. ruler

44. watermelon

45. straw

46. snowman

47. spaghetti

48. fence

49. fire

50. beach

51. sugar

52. stamp

53. pen

54. window

55. chicken

56. shampoo

57. candle

58. door

59. fish

60. bed

61. key

62. train

63. suitcase

64. wolf

65. bread

66. lightning

67. skirt

68. moon

69. newspaper

70. birthday cake

71. scarf

72. carrot

73. necklace

74. stop sign

75. piano

76. tambourine

77. scale

78. gas station

79. splinter

80. ditch

I.E.P. Goal: The student will generate adjectives to describe common nouns with 90% or greater accuracy.

Defining and Describing   131

Name _____

Tell how the following items are alike.   The first one is done for you.

1. crayon • marker
   (*You can color with them.*
   You can hold both in your hand.)

2. sweater • coat

3. scissors • knife

4. bus • taxicab

5. tie • scarf

6. elbow • knee

7. tissue • handkerchief

8. book • magazine

9. alarm clock • watch

10. gloves • mittens

11. shower • bath

12. horse • zebra

13. harmonica • trumpet

14. tennis shoes • slippers

15. mustache • beard

16. bench • couch

17. calf • puppy

18. uncle • grandfather

19. apple • tomato

20. ladder • flight of stairs

21. cotton ball • feather

22. bubbles • balloons

23. nail • thumbtack

24. suitcase • backpack

25. road • driveway

26. pajamas • nightgown

27. splinter • needle

28. raft • boat

29. guitar • violin

30. bicycle • motorcycle

31. creek • river

32. apartment • house

33. dictionary • encyclopedia

34. button • zipper

35. video camera • tape recorder

36. saw • axe

37. moon • star

38. contact lenses • glasses

39. deodorant • perfume

40. telescope • binoculars

I.E.P. Goal: The student will identify similar attributes or functions of common nouns with 90% or greater accuracy.

Defining and Describing   132

 **Lesson 8**

Tell how the following items are different.   The first one is done for you.

1. truck • boat
   (*A truck is different from a boat because a truck goes on land and a boat goes on water.*)

2. nose • ear

3. sister • brother

4. broom • vacuum cleaner

5. elephant • fox

6. drum • guitar

7. watermelon • apple

8. hug • kiss

9. marble • bowling ball

10. ketchup • mustard

11. ring • bracelet

12. washcloth • towel

13. roller skates • ice skates

14. gloves • mittens

15. milk • juice

16. rain • snow

17. train • car

18. lion • tiger

19. tree • rose

20. suitcase • purse

21. hammer • saw

22. sunglasses • eyeglasses

23. lime • lemon

24. beach • mountaintop

25. sun • moon

26. zipper • button

27. square • triangle

28. light bulb • candle

29. laugh • cry

30. bird • airplane

31. sneeze • cough

32. doctor • fire fighter

33. library • grocery store

34. shampoo • toothpaste

35. pizza • spaghetti

36. potato • carrot

37. basement • attic

38. kite • balloon

39. string • rope

40. waterfall • shower

I.E.P. Goal: The student will discriminate between similar items by identifying dissimilar attributes with 90% or greater accuracy.

Defining and Describing   133

Written Language

The mastery of written language is an important step in developing and refining good communication skills. Written language gives us another channel for sending and receiving messages, storing information, and expressing thoughts and feelings. We are frequently called upon to use written language in our daily activities to clarify and supplement spoken language. By improving their written language skills, children can develop yet another channel of communication.

There is a natural progression of written language skills in this unit. Initially, open-ended sentences are provided in a variety of contexts. Cues are gradually faded, providing less information to aid sentence completion. The next several tasks concentrate on constructing and breaking down compound and complex sentences followed by emphasis on expanding sentences and combining information to make sentences. Finally, the tasks move to the paragraph level. The student completes paragraphs with the correct parts of speech and then sequences sentences to construct paragraphs.

As your students complete these tasks, they will gain an increased awareness of the various aspects of written language. This new awareness will help them become better readers, writers, and speakers as they enrich their general language skills.

Name _____

Finish each sentence by writing the name of the picture in the blank.   The first one is done for you.

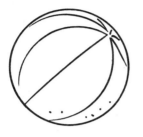

1. Kick the __ball_____ .

2. Maria drives a _____ .

3. I see a bumble _____ .

4. Cut the cake with a _____ .

5. Trey climbs a _____ .

6. Please turn on the _____ .

7. Open the door with a _____ .

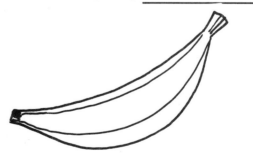

8. Jake peeled the _____ .

I.E.P. Goal: *Given picture cues, the student will complete sentences with the appropriate words with 90% or greater accuracy.*

Name _____

Finish each sentence by writing the name of the picture in the blank.

9. The sick child went to a
_____.

10. Joan put her _____ on
the shelf.

11. Toby rides a _____ to
school.

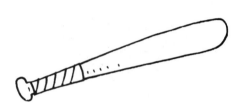

12. Jaymie swings the _____
at the ball.

13. The _____ fell and broke.

14. Her _____ was too small.

15. He put his _____ on
his head.

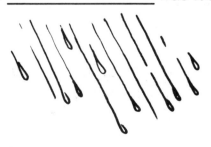

16. It looks like it will _____.

*I.E.P. Goal: Given picture cues, the student will complete sentences with the appropriate words with 90% or
greater accuracy.*

Name _____

Finish each sentence by writing the name of the picture in the blank.

17. The _____ has stopped.

18. Matt's _____ was red.

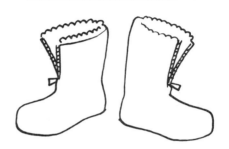

19. The _____ was tiny.

20. He wore his _____ to school.

21. They raised the _____.

22. Beth saw an _____ at the zoo.

23. I need a _____ for my letter.

24. The _____ was very funny.

I.E.P. Goal: *Given picture cues, the student will complete sentences with the appropriate words with 90% or greater accuracy.*

Written Language

137

Name _____

Fill in the blanks to make sentences that make sense.   The first one is done for you.

1. My father drives a __*car*_____.

2. The child colored the _____.

3. My hands are cold.   I need some _____.

4. I'm thirsty.   I'd like a _____.

5. The program is on at 8 o'clock.   Please turn on the _____.

6. I wash my face with soap and _____.

7. I'm so sleepy.   I need to go to _____.

8. Harry wants mustard, ketchup, and pickles on his _____.

9. Anna used the _____ to call her friend.

10. Some children get up early each morning to catch the _____.

11. The boys kicked the _____ to each other.

12. My dad buys our food at the _____.

13. Bonnie wore the bracelet on her _____.

14. Carl puts _____ on his toast.

15. We visit a _____ for a check-up.

16. Some people wear _____ on their fingers.

17. The teacher erases the _____ at the end of the day.

18. At the movies, David bought a drink and some _____.

19. Some people take showers and some take _____.

20. The bird flew high up in the _____.

I.E.P. Goal: The student will complete sentences with contextual cues by adding appropriate words with 90% or greater accuracy.

 More **Lesson 2**

Name _____

Fill in the blanks to make sentences that make sense.

21. Michael holds his pants up with a _____.

22. Bob brushed his teeth with a _____ and _____.

23. John needed a _____ to blow his nose.

24. You can keep your money in a _____.

25. Dan heated his soup on the _____.

26. The hairdresser used _____ to cut the boy's hair.

27. During a summer storm, we see lightning and hear _____.

28. A football player wears a _____ to protect his head.

29. My mother reads the _____ every morning before work.

30. My _____ wakes me up every morning.

31. The camper used a _____ to light the fire.

32. Hal packed his clothes in the _____ for his trip.

33. Eva put new film in her _____.

34. On windy days we like to fly our _____.

35. The birthday cake has six _____ on it.

36. The lumberjack chopped down the _____.

37. Tom put a _____ on the envelope before he mailed it.

38. Children eat their lunches in the school _____.

39. You say, " _____ " when someone is kind to you.

40. We see the sun in the day and the _____ at night.

I.E.P. Goal: *The student will complete sentences with contextual cues by adding appropriate words with 90% or greater accuracy.*

Name _____

Fill in the blanks to complete the steps for each activity.   The first one is started for you.

1. feeding the dog

Get out a clean dog _dish_____.

Open the bag of _____.

_____ the food in the bowl.

Give the dog fresh _____ to drink.

2. getting ready for school

Put on your school _____.

Eat your _____.

Brush your _____.

Comb your _____.

3. borrowing a library book

Choose the _____ you want.

Go to the check-out _____.

Get out your library _____.

_____ the librarian for helping you.

4. doing a homework assignment

Get some paper and a _____.

Open the _____ to the assignment.

_____ the directions.

Write your answers on the _____.

5. calling a friend

Find the number in the _____.

Pick up the _____.

Dial the _____.

Ask for your _____.

I.E.P. Goal: *The student will complete sentences to outline steps for performing common activities with 90% or greater accuracy.*

Name _____

Fill in the blanks to complete the steps for each activity.

6. washing your hair

Get your hair wet with some _____.

Use _____ to wash your hair.

Rinse your _____ with water.

Dry your hair with a _____.

7. wrapping a present

Use some scissors to cut the _____.

Put the paper around the _____.

Hold the paper together with _____.

Put a pretty _____ on top.

8. writing a letter to a friend

Take out a sheet of _____.

Get a _____ to write with.

Look up your friend's _____.

Put the letter in an _____ to mail.

9. taking out the trash

Get a big _____ bag.

Empty all the _____ into the bag.

_____ the bag.

Take the bag _____.

10. mowing the grass

Get out the _____.

Put _____ in the tank.

Pull the cord to start the _____.

Push the mower across the _____.

I.E.P. Goal: *The student will complete sentences to outline steps for performing common activities with 90% or greater accuracy.*

Written Language

Name _____

Make each sentence longer by adding one or two words.   The first one is done for you.

1. Dan loves eggs.

   Dan loves scrambled eggs. _____

2. I see a dog.

   _____

3. Karl climbs a tree.

   _____

4. Jane draws a picture.

   _____

5. Bonnie eats ice cream.

   _____

6. Gail reads the book.

   _____

7. Jay blew up the balloon.

   _____

8. Matt sweeps the floor.

   _____

9. Ivan broke the glass.

   _____

10. Ben steps in a hole.

   _____

I.E.P. Goal: **The student will use adjectives and adverbs to expand simple sentences with 90% or greater accuracy.**

Make each sentence longer by adding one or two words.

11. Laura sleeps in her bed.

_____

12. George pulls the wagon.

_____

13. Melanie tasted the lemon.

_____

14. The teacher shut the door.

_____

15. James helped the woman.

_____

16. Juan's shoes were too big.

_____

17. The bookshelves in Dave's room are full.

_____

18. They went into the room.

_____

19. Brian combs his hair.

_____

20. Oscar touched the rock.

_____

I.E.P. Goal: **The student will use adjectives and adverbs to expand simple sentences with 90% or greater accuracy.**

Make each sentence longer by adding one or two words.

21. The toy wouldn't work.

_____

22. My friends skate on the lake.

_____

23. The drink was refreshing.

_____

24. We laughed at the movie.

_____

25. You must be quiet in the library.

_____

26. The man snored in his sleep.

_____

27. The rabbits hop through the bushes.

_____

28. Tom saw the star in the sky.

_____

29. The toast was black.

_____

30. Turtles crawl over the rocks.

_____

I.E.P. Goal: The student will use adjectives and adverbs to expand simple sentences with 90% or greater accuracy.

Name _____

Use the information below to answer the questions.   Write your answers in complete sentences.
The first one is done for you.

1. bowl
   cereal
   milk

   What did Donna eat this morning?

   She ate cereal for breakfast. _____

2. pajamas
   toothbrush
   slippers

   What did Sally do at night?

   _____

3. camera
   film
   flashbulb

   What was Larry going to do?

   _____

4. raincoat
   umbrella
   rain boots

   What was Alice getting ready to do?

   _____

5. yellow bus
   backpack
   lunch
   homework

   Where was Alan going today?

   _____

6. presents
   cake with candles
   balloons
   party hats

   What did the Barnes family do this afternoon?

   _____

*I.E.P. Goal: The student will use the information provided to respond to questions in sentence form with 90% or
        greater accuracy.*

Use the information below to answer the questions.   Write your answers in complete sentences.

7. children
    swings
    jungle gym
    slide

Where did Mrs. James go today?

_____

8. red truck
    siren
    hoses
    ladders

What did Mark see this morning?

_____

9. wind
    kite
    string
    open field

What did Jamie do today?

_____

10. pond
    bathing suit
    lifeguard
    towel

What was Pam going to do this afternoon?

_____

11. giraffes
    cages
    monkeys
    bears

Where did we go on our field trip?

_____

12. basket
    blanket
    food
    spring day

What did the Harris family do today?

_____

I.E.P. Goal: The student will use the information provided to respond to questions in sentence form with 90% or greater accuracy.

Name _____

Use the information below to answer the questions.   Write your answers in complete sentences.

13. bicycle
    helmet
    water bottle
    map

    What was Jerry going to do?

    _____

14. gym
    teams
    basketballs
    fans

    What did Brian do today?

    _____

15. barn
    pasture
    pigs
    tractor

    Where did the fourth grade go yesterday?

    _____

16. shopping carts
    coupons
    food
    checkout counter

    Where did Mrs. Davis go this afternoon?

    _____

17. schedule
    TV
    VCR
    videotape

    What was Matt going to do?

    _____

18. astronaut
    space shuttle
    satellites
    planets

    Where can these be found?

    _____

I.E.P. Goal: The student will use the information provided to respond to questions in sentence form with 90% or
        greater accuracy.

Lesson 6

Name _____

Complete each paragraph by filling in the blanks with the correct words.   A hint is provided under each blank.   The first one is started for you.

1. For breakfast, I like to eat _____*cereal*_____.   Orange juice is my favorite thing to

                                noun

  _____*drink*_____.   I need a _____ and a spoon to _____

       verb   noun   verb

  my cereal.   Don't pour on too much _____ or your cereal will get soggy!

                                           noun

2. Yesterday, Sam and I went to the playground to _____.   He likes to slide

                                        verb

  down the _____.   I like to _____ on the jungle gym.   We

                noun   verb

  have lots of races to see who can _____ the fastest.   Sam is my best

                                   verb

  _____.

    noun

3. My favorite musical instrument is the _____.   Sherry _____

                                 noun   verb

  the piano and Michael beats on the _____.   You have to _____

                                noun   verb

  pretty hard to play the trumpet.   We all go to _____ once a week to learn

                                       noun

  how to read music.   One day, maybe, we'll all be in the high school marching

  _____.

    noun

4. The _____ snow was six inches deep.   The kids didn't have to go to

            adjective

  _____ this morning.   Instead, they put on coats and hats.   Then, they

    noun

  put _____ on their feet and _____ on their hands and went

        noun   noun

  out to play.   The kids built a big _____ and _____ snowballs

                          noun   verb

  at each other all afternoon.   When they all got _____, they went inside and

                                         adjective

  drank _____ chocolate.

       adjective

I.E.P. Goal: Given parts of speech cues, the student will complete paragraphs with appropriate words with 90% or greater accuracy.

Name _____

Complete each paragraph by filling in the blanks with the correct words.   A hint is provided under each blank.

5. The paper carrier brings us the _____ every morning.   My father
                                    noun

    _____ it while he _____ his breakfast.   His favorite page
         verb   verb

    is the sports _____.   During the week, the _____ is thin.
                       noun   noun

    On Sundays, the newspaper is _____ thick.
                                       adverb

6. Jan had a birthday _____ with her family.   Jan was four _____
                            noun   noun

    old.   Jan's dad baked her a _____ birthday cake and put four
                                      adjective

    _____ on it.   When the candles were lit, they were very _____.
         noun   adjective

    Jan's dad _____ the cake into small pieces.   They also had some vanilla
                   verb

    and _____ ice cream that was very _____.   Jan's little sister
            adjective   adjective

    wants her dad to _____ her _____ cake when she turns three.
                          verb   adjective

7. Arnie wanted to get a dog for a _____.   He couldn't decide if he should get
                                         noun

    a big dog or a _____ one.   His father told him he would have to
                        adjective

    _____ the dog every day and take him on a _____ for exercise.
         verb   noun

    Arnie's friend Jake had a _____ named Sandy.   Sandy had a litter of
                                   noun

    _____.   Jake gave Arnie the _____ puppy, which he named
         noun   adjective

    Clancy.

I.E.P. Goal: Given parts of speech cues, the student will complete paragraphs with appropriate words with 90% or greater accuracy.

Name _____

Complete each paragraph by filling in the blanks with the correct words.   A hint is provided under each blank.

8. Last night, Dan had a _____ dream.   He thought he was locked in a haunted
                                 adjective

    _____ alone.   It was so _____, he couldn't see anything.   He
         noun   adjective

    could _____ strange noises coming from upstairs, but he was too
              verb

    _____ to find out what was making them.   As Dan slowly moved
         adjective

    _____ the door, there was a bright flash of _____.   His
         preposition   noun

    grandma had turned on the light and Dan was in his own _____.
                                                                     noun

9. Sheila had a _____ cold.   She sneezed so much that she used a whole box
                      adjective

    of _____.   She finally went to see her _____, who gave her
            noun   noun

    some _____ to take.   Now she feels _____ better.   At least
             noun   adverb

    she doesn't have to _____ her nose so often.
                              verb

10. The first-grade class was going on a field _____ to the zoo.   Each person
                                                        noun

     needed to _____ a lunch in a paper bag.   They all climbed in a
                     verb

     _____ and rode to the zoo.   The children were amazed by how
          noun

     _____ the elephants were and how _____ the snakes were.
          adjective   adjective

     The children all _____ jackets because it was a _____ day.
                            verb   adjective

     It took about an hour for them to walk _____ the entire zoo.   Then, they
                                                    preposition

     _____ at picnic tables and _____ their lunches.   The children
          verb   verb

     all said they wanted to come back _____.
                                             adverb

*I.E.P. Goal: Given parts of speech cues, the student will complete paragraphs with appropriate words with 90%
          or greater accuracy.*

Written Language   150

Name _____

Read the title for each paragraph.   Then, put each group of sentences in order to make a logical paragraph.   Finally, write the sentences in order on another piece of paper.   The first one is done for you.

1. Title: **Bedtime at Our House**

   ___1___   I put on my pajamas.

   ___3___   We turn off the light.

   ___2___   My mom reads me a story in bed.

2. Title: **Playground Fun**

   _____   We swing, slide, and run.

   _____   We go home at lunchtime.

   _____   We go to the playground every Saturday morning.

3. Title: **The Sandwich Maker**

   _____   He can't make any other kind.

   _____   Bobby makes only peanut butter and jelly sandwiches.

   _____   He really should be called the "PB&J Sandwich Maker."

4. Title: **April's New Camera**

   _____   April likes this camera better.

   _____   April broke her old camera.

   _____   Her uncle got her a new one.

5. Title: **Roller Skating Is Fun**

   _____   They skated for one hour.

   _____   It was lots of fun.

   _____   Melissa invited Iva to go skating.

I.E.P. Goal: The student will sequence sentences into logical paragraphs with 90% or greater accuracy.

Written Language   151

Name _____

Read the title for each paragraph.   Then, put each group of sentences in order to make a logical paragraph.   Finally, write the sentences in order on another piece of paper.

6. Title: **Walking the Dog**

_____ Bo needed some water when they got home.

_____ They walked around the block two times.

_____ Fred put the leash on his dog Bo.

7. Title: **A Visit to the Fire Station**

_____ We went to the fire station today.

_____ I hope we can go back soon.

_____ The fire fighters let us turn on the siren.

8. Title: **Summer Vacation**

_____ Sue is going to the beach.

_____ Sue can't wait for summer vacation.

_____ Sue won't be back for two weeks.

9. Title: **The Purple Dress**

_____ She and her mom went shopping for it yesterday.

_____ Chris wanted a purple dress.

_____ It went perfectly with her new shoes.

10. Title: **My Favorite Necklace**

_____ It is my favorite one.

_____ I hope I'll get a bracelet to match.

_____ My aunt gave me a necklace.

*I.E.P. Goal: The student will sequence sentences into logical paragraphs with **90% or greater accuracy.***

Read the title for each paragraph.   Then, put each group of sentences in order to make a logical paragraph.   Finally, write the sentences in order on another piece of paper.

11. Title: **Camping Out**

_____ Maybe our troop will go there next year.

_____ They hiked to the mountain peak.

_____ After they reached the top, they pitched their tents.

_____ The Scouts went camping last weekend.

12. Title: **The Quiet Pet**

_____ My friend is allergic to dogs and cats.

_____ They aren't hard to take care of.

_____ And, her parents like them because they're quiet.

_____ So, I suggested she get some fish.

13. Title: **The Book Report**

_____ We could choose from three books.

_____ I picked the shortest one.

_____ My book report was short, too!

_____ Our teacher assigned a book report.

14. Title: **The Airport**

_____ Jill hugged us all good-bye.

_____ We all watched her plane take off.

_____ She paid for her ticket and checked her bag.

_____ We took Jill to the airport for her flight.

I.E.P. Goal: The student will sequence sentences into logical paragraphs with 90% or greater accuracy.

Processing Information

During children's daily activities at home, school, and in the neighborhood, they are constantly confronted with information. Information is presented in many forms and contexts from a variety of sources. Students with communication deficits often have difficulty attending to, processing, and acting upon information appropriately. As a result, they may miss information important to their safety and well-being, academic progress, and interactions with others.

The lessons in this section provide students with practice receiving, organizing, and relaying information. Throughout the tasks, opportunities are provided to help students organize and retrieve information, enabling them to function more independently, safely, and effectively in their daily environments.

Name _____

Read the steps under each activity.   Then, number them in the correct order.   The first one is done for you.

1. Washing your hands

    _2_ Rub your hands together.

    _1_ Put soap on your hands.

    _3_ Rinse off the soap.

2. Taking a shower

    ____ Dry off with a towel.

    ____ Turn on the water.

    ____ Wash with soap.

3. Putting on tennis shoes

    ____ Tighten the laces.

    ____ Put the shoe on your foot.

    ____ Tie a bow in the laces.

4. Making a ham sandwich

    ____ Cut the sandwich in half.

    ____ Get two slices of bread from the bag.

    ____ Place ham on the bread.

5. Going to school

    ____ Get in the car or on the bus.

    ____ Wake up.

    ____ Get dressed.

6. Making ice

    ____ Put the ice cube tray in the freezer.

    ____ Fill the ice cube tray with water.

    ____ Wait until the ice is frozen.

7. Making a telephone call

    ____ Look up the phone number.

    ____ Dial the phone number.

    ____ Pick up the telephone receiver.

8. Taping a song on the tape recorder

    ____ Sing into the microphone.

    ____ Put a tape into the tape recorder.

    ____ Push the "record" button.

9. Buying a new pair of jeans

    ____ Pay for the jeans.

    ____ Try on the jeans.

    ____ Find some jeans you might like.

10. Washing your bicycle

    ____ Wash the bicycle with a soapy rag.

    ____ Rinse off the soap with a hose.

    ____ Dry off the seat with a rag.

I.E.P. Goal: The student will sequence instructions for tasks with 90% or greater accuracy.

Processing Information

More **Lesson 1**

Name _____

Read the steps under each activity.   Then, number them in the correct order.

11. Making a house from a cardboard box

____ Cut out the door and windows.

____ Mark the lines for the door and windows.

____ Turn the box upside down.

12. Making a birthday card

____ Put the card in an envelope.

____ Fold a piece of paper in half.

____ Draw a picture and write "Happy Birthday" on the card.

____ Get out some markers and paper.

13. Taking a photograph

____ Look into the camera.

____ Put film in the camera.

____ Push the button.

____ Tell everyone to say "cheese."

14. Going grocery shopping

____ Put the food into the cart.

____ Put the food on the check-out counter.

____ Pay for the food.

____ Get a grocery cart.

15. Feeding your cat

____ Use a spoon to put the food into the bowl.

____ Find the cat's bowl.

____ Open the cat food with a can opener.

____ Put the bowl on the floor and call the cat.

16. Going to the movies

____ Buy your ticket.

____ Give your ticket to the usher.

____ Look in the paper to see what movies are playing.

____ Decide which movie you want to see.

17. Playing a tape on the VCR

____ Push "play."

____ Turn the machine on.

____ Put the tape into the machine.

____ Turn the machine off.

18. Adding two-digit numbers

____ Add the numbers in the left-hand column.

____ Write the numbers in a column one underneath the other.

____ Add the numbers in the right-hand column.

____ Draw a line under the numbers on your paper.

I.E.P. Goal: The student will sequence instructions for tasks with 90% or greater accuracy.

Processing Information   156

Name _____

Follow each direction.   Put the items in order.   The first one is done for you.

1. Order these animals from biggest to littlest:

   _1_ horse

   _2_ dog

   _3_ mouse

6. Order these items from lightest to heaviest:

   ____ paper clip

   ____ hammer

   ____ hairbrush

2. Order these foods from smallest to largest:

   ____ raisin

   ____ apple

   ____ watermelon

7. Order these items from longest to shortest:

   ____ crayon

   ____ ruler

   ____ broom

3. Order these items from largest to smallest:

   ____ stamp

   ____ piece of notebook paper

   ____ piece of newspaper

8. Order these foods from hottest to coldest:

   ____ ice cream

   ____ peanut butter

   ____ hot chocolate

4. Order these items from smallest to biggest:

   ____ soccer ball

   ____ marble

   ____ baseball

9. Order these items from shortest to longest:

   ____ minute

   ____ day

   ____ hour

5. Order these items from heaviest to lightest:

   ____ slice of bread

   ____ telephone book

   ____ bowling ball

10. Order these people from oldest to youngest:

   ____ grandmother

   ____ child

   ____ mother

I.E.P. Goal: The student will order items according to specified attributes with 90% or greater accuracy.

Processing Information   157

More **Lesson 2**

Name _____

Follow each direction.   Put the items in order.

11. Order these items from hardest to softest:
    ____ pillow
    ____ brick
    ____ eraser

12. Order these items from quietest to loudest:
    ____ ticking watch
    ____ doorbell
    ____ moving train

13. Order these animals from shortest to tallest:
    ____ giraffe
    ____ monkey
    ____ robin

14. Order these items from thinnest to fattest:
    ____ banana
    ____ finger
    ____ strand of hair

15. Order these ways of traveling from fastest to slowest:
    ____ bicycle
    ____ jet
    ____ train

16. Order these clothing items from the thickest to thinnest:
    ____ T-shirt
    ____ coat
    ____ sweatshirt

17. Order these seasons from coolest to warmest:
    ____ winter
    ____ spring
    ____ summer

18. Order these utensils from sharpest to dullest:
    ____ knife
    ____ spoon
    ____ fork

19. Order these animals, beginning with the slowest:
    ____ deer
    ____ cat
    ____ turtle

I.E.P. Goal: The student will order items according to specified attributes with 90% or greater accuracy.

Processing Information

Name _____

Follow each direction.   Put the items in order.

20. Order these items, beginning with the one that holds the most liquid:

____ milk jug

____ teaspoon

____ cup

21. Order these items, beginning with the noisiest one:

____ frog

____ rooster

____ hermit crab

22. Order these sports, beginning with the one that involves the most players at one time:

____ basketball

____ tennis

____ diving

23. Order these items, beginning with the one that costs the most:

____ candy bar

____ notebook

____ motorcycle

____ roller skates

24. Order these animals in alphabetical order:

____ canary

____ goat

____ zebra

____ lizard

25. Order these money names, beginning with the one that is worth the least:

____ nickel

____ dollar

____ quarter

____ penny

26. Order these measurements, beginning with the smallest:

____ mile

____ yard

____ inch

____ foot

27. Order these historical events, beginning with the one that happened first:

____ a person walked on the moon

____ dinosaurs roamed the earth

____ America became a country

____ the telephone was invented

I.E.P. Goal: The student will order items according to specified attributes with 90% or greater accuracy.

Lesson 3

Name _____

Complete the tasks from the material listed.   (Note: Modify requests as needed.)

1. Use a children's picture book to:

   a.   tell me what is on the cover.

   b.   find the first page.

   c.   show me a picture of a boy or girl.

   d.   find page 10.

   e.   find a picture of a car.

   f.   find a page with blue on it.

   g.   find the last page.

3. Use a schedule of your school day to:

   a.   tell what time school starts.

   b.   tell which subject you study first in the morning.

   c.   tell what time you go to lunch.

   d.   tell which subject you study last before going home.

   e.   tell when you have recess.

   f.   tell what you do after you have reading.

   g.   tell what you do after you have lunch.

2. Use your reading (text) book to:

   a.   show me the title of the book.

   b.   find the first story.

   c.   find a story about an animal.

   d.   find the table of contents.

   e.   tell me how many pages are in the book.

   f.   find your favorite story in the book.

   g.   tell me who wrote your favorite story.

4. Use your spelling book to:

   a.   find three spelling words that start with "b."

   b.   find two spelling words that end with "ing."

   c.   tell me the first word in the first list.

   d.   tell me the last word in the last list.

   e.   tell me the number of pages in the book.

   f.   find a word with three or more syllables.

   g.   find a spelling word that begins with the first letter of your last name.

I.E.P. Goal: The student will use materials to find requested information with 90% or greater accuracy.

Processing Information

 More Lesson 3

Name _____

Complete the tasks from the material listed.   (Note: Modify requests as needed.)

5. Use a school directory or yearbook to:

 a. find the full name of the school.

 b. find the principal's full name.

 c. tell how many second grade teachers there are.

 d. tell how many grades are taught.

 e. tell if there are any male teachers.

 f. find out how many teachers teach a special subject rather than a certain grade.

 g. find the name of the custodian.

7. Use a map of your state to:

 a. find the city you live in.

 b. find the capital.

 c. find another large city that is not the capital.

 d. find a river, lake, or ocean that is in or near your state.

 e. find the name of a city that is two words.

 f. tell what borders your state on the north.

 g. tell what borders your state on the east.

6. Use your school's monthly lunch menu to:

 a. tell what we're having for lunch today.

 b. find out how many times we're having something you like.

 c. name three different vegetables that are served.

 d. tell the first time fish sticks are served.

 e. name all the desserts that are served.

 f. tell what is being served on the last day of the menu.

 g. tell what food is served the most often.

8. Use a map of the United States to:

 a. find Washington D.C.

 b. find your state.

 c. find a state that borders an ocean.

 d. find a state that borders Canada.

 e. find the Mississippi River.

 f. find the largest state.

 g. find the smallest state.

I.E.P. Goal: The student will use materials to find requested information with 90% or greater accuracy.

Lesson 4

Name _____

Toy Store

Look at the picture.   Then, answer the questions below.   The first one is done for you.

1. How many dolls are on the top shelf?   _*three*_____

2. What is between the teddy bear and the rabbit? _____

3. What is under the airplane? _____

4. Who is standing behind the blocks? _____

5. What is above the train? _____

6. What is beneath the rabbit? _____

7. What is in front of the bike? _____

8. What is inside the wagon? _____

9. What is over the books? _____

10. What is beside the airplane? _____

I.E.P. Goal: The student will answer directional questions using maps and diagrams with 90% or greater accuracy.

Processing Information   162

Name _____

Barnyard

Look at the picture.   Then, answer the questions below.   The first one is done for you.

1. What is next to the barn?   _henhouse_____

2. What is between the henhouse and the fence? _____

3. What is on top of the barn? _____

4. What is crawling under the fence? _____

5. What is on top of the henhouse? _____

6. Which animal is in the middle of the corral? _____

7. What is on each side of the henhouse? _____

8. Which animals are indoors? _____

9. How many different kinds of animals are in the picture? _____

10. Which animal appears most in the picture? _____

I.E.P. Goal: The student will answer directional questions using maps and diagrams with 90% or greater accuracy.

Name _____

Classroom

Look at the picture.   Then, answer the questions below.   The first one is done for you.

1. Whose desk is closest to the door?   *the teacher's* _____

2. What is on the wall behind the teacher's desk? _____

3. What is on the wall across from the teacher's desk? _____

4. What is between the bookshelves and the tape player? _____

5. How many desks are in the middle row? _____

6. How many chairs are on the rug? _____

7. How many chairs are beside the rug? _____

8. What is next to the clock? _____

9. What is over the bookshelves? _____

10. What is under the clock? _____

I.E.P. Goal: The student will answer directional questions using maps and diagrams with 90% or greater accuracy.

Name _____

Kitchen

Look at the picture.   Then, answer the questions below.   The first one is done for you.

1. What is on the rug?   *a cat* _____

2. What is on the refrigerator? _____

3. What is between the knife and the refrigerator? _____

4. What is in front of the refrigerator? _____

5. What is above the sink? _____

6. What is on top of the dishwasher? _____

7. What is beneath the clock? _____

8. What is between the bowl of fruit and the scissors? _____

9. What is to the right of the stove? _____

10. What is to the left of the sink? _____

I.E.P. Goal: The student will answer directional questions using maps and diagrams with 90% or greater accuracy.

Processing Information   165

Name _____

Playground

Look at the picture.   Then, answer the questions below.   The first one is done for you.

1. What is in the middle of the playground?   _merry-go-round_____

2. What piece of playground equipment is closest to the entrance?   _____

3. What is between the bench and the jungle gym?   _____

4. What is on either side of the water fountain?   _____

5. What is between the water fountain and the seesaw?   _____

6. If you follow the arrows, what do you come to first?   _____

7. If you follow the arrows, what do you pass after the water fountain?   _____

8. What is on the right-hand side of the playground?   _____

9. What is on the left-hand side of the playground?   _____

10. If you walk straight across the playground from the seesaw, which piece of playground

    equipment will you run into?   _____

I.E.P. Goal: The student will answer directional questions using maps and diagrams with 90% or greater accuracy.

Campground

Look at the picture.   Then, answer the questions below.   The first one is done for you.

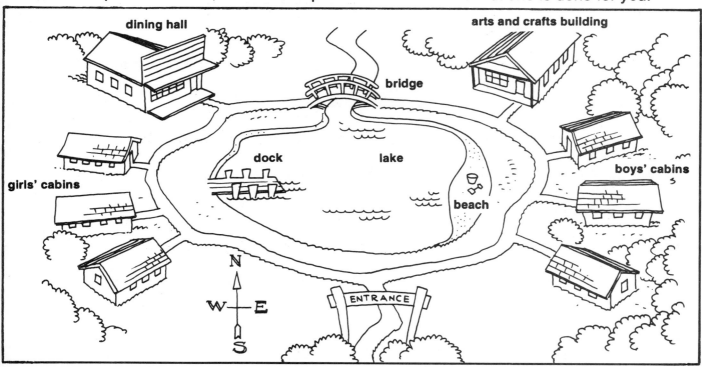

1. If you stand on the dock and look east, whose cabins do you see?   _boys'_

2. If you stand on the dock and look west, whose cabins do you see?   _____

3. Whose cabins are to the south of the dining hall?   _____

4. Whose cabins are farthest from the dock?   _____

5. Whose cabins are to the south of the arts and crafts building?   _____

6. What is to the north of the lake?   _____

7. If you dive off the dock and swim east, where will you be?   _____

8. If you stand on the bridge and look south, what do you see?   _____

9. If you stand at the entrance and look north, what do you see?   _____

10. Which building is west of the arts and crafts building?   _____

I.E.P. Goal: The student will answer directional questions using maps and diagrams with 90% or greater accuracy.

Name _____

Underline the sentence that doesn't belong in each item.   The first one is done for you.

1. My cat is lost.   I've looked everywhere.   <u>My favorite color is red.</u>

2. My shirt is wet.   I ordered a hamburger.   I also got french fries.

3. I spilled juice on the floor.   Squirrels like nuts.   Be careful you don't step in the juice.

4. My name is Rose.   I'm ten years old.   Knives are sharp.

5. I like to make popcorn.   Sometimes I sprinkle cheese on it.   My bike has a flat tire.

6. I need new shoes.   Pickles are sour.   My old shoes are too small.

7. Yesterday it snowed.   The clock has stopped.   Don't wind it too tight.

8. My dad runs marathon races.   The pie is hot.   He won a race last week.

9. The lawn mower is noisy.   Skunks are black and white.   Another black and white animal is a zebra.

10. My brother has a new car.   It cost a lot of money.   My dog likes to eat ice cream.

11. It was dark in the movie theater.   I hit my finger with a hammer.   I dropped a quarter under my seat but couldn't find it.

12. My sister goes to college.   She wants to be a teacher.   Our neighbor drives a truck.

13. The doorbell keeps buzzing.   The noise is annoying.   The clothes in the dryer are still wet.

14. My father works for the city.   I'm working on a science project.   I'm making a model of an underground cave.

15. We're having pizza for lunch.   I'm going to wear my blue dress to the party.   Would you like to eat lunch with us?

16. Kevin is moving to Vermont.   Wednesday is his last day of school.   My aunt lives in California.

17. My teacher's name is Mrs. Wood.   She has brown hair and brown eyes.   My dad and I went for a walk in the woods.

I.E.P. Goal: The student will identify irrelevant information in short paragraphs with 90% or greater accuracy.

Processing Information

Name _____

Underline the sentence that doesn't belong in each item.

18. You should drink lots of water.   Bears can be dangerous.   It helps you stay healthy.

19. Lucy's birthday was July 4th.   She had sparklers on her cake.   Memorial Day is in May.

20. First, wrap the rolls in foil.   Put them in a hot oven.   Too much salt will ruin the soup.

21. Oranges are a citrus fruit.   Bacon tastes good with pancakes.   Limes and lemons are also citrus fruits.

22. If you watch too much television, you won't get enough exercise.   One to two hours of TV a day is enough.   Be careful when you use a hair dryer.

23. Our family has a reunion every summer.   Relatives come from all across the country. Last year, there were over a hundred people.   Why don't you look for the bus?

24. Joe's brother is a hockey star.   My sister wears hearing aids.   She got them when she was three years old.   Without them, she can't hear what people say.

25. When they clean our street, we have to move our cars to the other side.   Once my dad forgot and he got a ticket.   My dad likes to play the piano.   Now, he always remembers to move the car.

26. Whenever we have a spelling test, I study very hard the night before.   Our room number is 17.   I want to get good grades on the tests.   My mom calls out the words to me while she fixes dinner.

27. Don't put your comb on the kitchen table.   Call me as soon as you get home.   My number is inside the red folder.   If I'm not there, leave a message with my father.

28. We need twelve students to help paint the scenery.   We have to start soon because the play is in two weeks.   If you can help, sign this list.   The math assignment begins on page five.

29. A baby sea lion is called a pup.   Sea lions are very graceful.   Blue jays are noisy.   Sea lions travel in groups called pods.

30. Goose feathers are called down.   A tool for carving wood is called a chisel.   Goose down is very warm.   It's used in pillows and jackets.

I.E.P. Goal: The student will identify irrelevant information in short paragraphs with 90% or greater accuracy.

Processing Information   169

Name _____

Circle the best message for each situation.   The first one is done for you.

1. Val's dog, Dexter, has run away.   Which message should she leave her mother?

   a. I've gone to look for Dexter.

   b. I'd like hamburgers for dinner.

2. Andy left his lunch in his father's car.   Which message should he leave him?

   a. I'm going to Luke's after school.

   b. I'm borrowing money to buy a school lunch.

3. Tanya's grandmother is celebrating her 80th birthday.   Which message should Tanya write on her grandmother's birthday card?

   a. I hope you have a wonderful day.

   b. Did you find my bracelet?

4. Steven received a package with someone else's name on it.   Which message should he leave for the mail carrier?

   a. This package is not mine.

   b. Bring another package soon.

5. Sylvia's best friend is absent from school.   Which message should Sylvia leave her?

   a. I hope you're okay.

   b. May I borrow your bike?

6. Elliot is going to be late for the Scout meeting.   Which message should he leave the troop leader?

   a. I finished my project.

   b. I'll be fifteen minutes late.

I.E.P. Goal: The student will choose appropriate messages to convey information in common situations with 90% or greater accuracy.

Processing Information   170

Name _____

Circle the best message for each situation.

7. Alvin's mother wants him to do some chores when he gets home from school. Which message should she leave him?

   a. There are some carrot sticks in the refrigerator.

   b. Please fold the clothes and wash the dishes.

8. Julie can't baby-sit tonight as she has promised. Which message should she leave the children's parents?

   a. I got a good grade on my test today.

   b. I'm sorry I can't baby-sit for your children tonight.

9. Jenny needs a ride home from dancing at 4:00. Which message should she leave her mother?

   a. Please pick me up from dancing at 4:00.

   b. Are you going to the store on the way home from work?

10. David and Carrie are going to the movies. Which message should David leave Carrie before he leaves his house?

   a. I'll meet you at the movies at two o'clock.

   b. My favorite actor is in this movie.

11. Tony wants Eric to come over to his apartment and work on a school project. Which message should he leave for Eric?

   a. Come listen to the new tape I got today.

   b. Can you work on our project this evening?

12. Jean's teacher, Mr. Hill, needs to talk to her parents. Which message should he leave for them?

   a. Please call Mr. Hill at school before five o'clock.

   b. Jean ate only half of her sandwich at lunch today.

I.E.P. Goal: The student will choose appropriate messages to convey information in common situations with 90% or greater accuracy.

Name _____

Circle the best message for each situation.

13. May wants her grandfather to help her fix her bike.   Which message should she leave him?

   a. Please bring your toolbox when you come for dinner.

   b. Did you know I can ride a two-wheeler now?

14. Betsy's aunt wants to take her shopping before her birthday.   Which message should she leave for Betsy?

   a. I want you to have a special birthday this year.

   b. I want to take you shopping before your birthday.

15. Ben's neighbor wants him to mow the lawn.   Which message should he leave for Ben?

   a. Our grass has grown very high.

   b. Ben, can you mow our lawn this weekend?

16. Mrs. Conti will be late for class.   Which message should she leave for her students?

   a. Begin working on page 37 in your social studies book.

   b. I finished reading everyone's book reports.

17. Alex's bus number has been changed.   Which message should Alex's teacher send to his parents?

   a. Alex's bus number has been changed to 15.

   b. Alex has a new bus number.

18. Eddie knocks on his neighbors' door but no one answers.   Which message should he leave for them?

   a. Sorry I missed you.   Eddie.

   b. I stopped by.

I.E.P. Goal: The student will choose appropriate messages to convey information in common situations with 90% or greater accuracy.

 **Lesson 7**

Name _____

Write a short message for each situation.   The first one is done for you.

1. It's your brother's turn to feed the dog.   Write a note so he won't forget.

   Feed the dog – don't forget!
   _____

2. There's a special show on television at 8:00 on Friday.   Make a note reminding yourself to watch it.

   _____

3. Carol needs to bring a sleeping bag to the party.   Write a note to help Carol remember.

   _____

4. Your father's birthday is on Monday.   Write a note to help you remember.

   _____

5. You must bring your library books to school tomorrow.   Write a note to help you remember.

   _____

6. Anna used the last piece of bread.   Write a note so her father will know to buy some more.

   _____

7. Your mother's friend Dora called.   Write a note telling your mother about the call.

   _____

8. Your grandmother called to invite you for dinner on Sunday.   Write a note telling the rest of the family about her call.

   _____

9. Your grandfather said he needs a new set of wrenches.   Make a note so you'll remember this for his birthday.

   _____

I.E.P. Goal: The student will write brief notes from information provided with 90% or greater accuracy.

Processing Information   173

Name _____

Write a short message for each situation.

10. You need to be at school by 7:30 on Friday to leave for a field trip.   Write a note to help you remember to go early.

_____

11. Shauntelle is going to play at Deana's house.   Write a note so her mother knows where she is.

_____

12. Your homework assignment is to do pages 5 and 6 in your math book.   Write a note to help you remember.

_____

13. The library is open on Monday and Wednesday evenings until 9:00.   Make a note of this schedule.

_____

14. The man from the garage called to tell your father that his car will be ready after 5:00. Write a note so your father knows to pick up his car.

_____

15. The movie you want to see is shown at 1:15, 4:00, and 7:30.   Make a note of the schedule for your friend.

_____

16. Mike needs two batteries for his radio, a pack of notebook paper, and a birthday present for his sister.   Write a note he can take to the store.

_____

17. You and your friends are ordering pizza.   You've agreed on a large pepperoni pizza with extra cheese and a small plain pizza.   Write a note to help you remember when you order.

_____

I.E.P. Goal: The student will write brief notes from information provided with 90% or greater accuracy.

Self-Expression

Much of an infant's oral expression is concerned with the communication of basic needs such as food, water, and comfort. These needs are essential for growth and survival. Early feelings and emotions are directly related to the satisfaction of these needs. As a child matures, she begins to experience different feelings and associate these emotions with events, people, and places. Later, these associations influence thinking and reasoning as personal opinions are developed.

Children with communication impairments often lack the ability to effectively communicate their most basic needs. If they are able to express basic needs, they may be unable to convey more complex expressions of feelings and opinions. Their conversation is often rote and repetitive. Within this section, activities familiarize the student with identification, interpretation, and expression of needs, opinions, and feelings within the context of daily living. Improvement in these skills results in an enrichment of the individual's language system and enables him to express his needs, feelings, and opinions in social situations.

Choose the items that go with each event.   The first one is done for you.

1. taking a bath

   (soap)   banana   (water)   hammer

2. going to school

   broom   books   bus   couch

3. brushing teeth

   hot dog   toothpaste   sweater   toothbrush

4. eating breakfast

   cereal   ruler   tree   spoon

5. coloring a picture

   car   markers   crayons   jacket

6. washing your hands

   soap   sink   attic   horse

7. doing homework

   paper   pencil   dessert   book

8. playing basketball

   ball   doorknob   hoop   celery

9. walking the dog

   milk   collar   saw   leash

10. keeping dry in the rain

   umbrella   raincoat   table   crayon

I.E.P. Goal: The student will match needed items with common events with 90% or greater accuracy.

Choose the items that go with each event.

11. riding a bicycle

   helmet   kitchen   handlebars   book

12. mailing a letter

   chair   stamp   envelope   alligator

13. making a bed

   sheets   quilt   garden   leaf

14. making a telephone call

   number   tool   phone   drum

15. setting the table

   bell   forks   napkins   hose

16. making a sandwich

   bandage   bread   tire   peanut butter

17. lighting a fire

   matches   wood   snow   bat

18. taking a picture

   lime   camera   bee   film

19. sweeping the floor

   key   dustpan   broom   ticket

20. keeping warm

   blanket   smile   coat   puddle

I.E.P. Goal: The student will match needed items with common events with 90% or greater accuracy.

Self-Expression   177

Name _____

Choose the items that go with each event.

21. grocery shopping

       sister   football   food   cart

22. cutting hair

       scissors   chain saw   clippers   orange

23. treating an illness

       costume   doctor   medicine   tractor

24. riding a horse

       saddle   peanut   brick   reins

25. growing flowers

       seeds   dirt   water   sled

26. making popcorn

       pie   kernels   oil   salt

27. blowing bubbles

       wand   liquid soap   refrigerator   slippers

28. checking out a book

       librarian   book   sandwich   shelves

29. making Jell-O

       bowl   broom   hot water   spoon

30. putting on a play

       tightrope   theater   actors   stroller

I.E.P. Goal: The student will match needed items with common events with 90% or greater accuracy.

Lesson 2

Name _____

Finish each sentence.   The first one is done for you.

1. To drink water, you need _a cup_____.

2. To color a picture, you need _____.

3. To cut hair, you need _____.

4. To brush your teeth, you need _____.

5. To write your name, you need _____.

6. To eat soup, you need _____.

7. To make toast, you need _____.

8. To dry yourself after a bath, you need _____.

9. To fix your hair, you need _____.

10. To see in the dark, you need _____.

11. To chew your food, you need _____.

12. To call a friend at home, you need _____.

13. To unlock the door, you need _____.

14. To cut your food, you need _____.

15. To keep your hands warm, you need _____.

16. To sit at the table, you need _____.

17. To sweep the floor, you need _____.

18. To take a picture, you need _____.

19. To cut down a tree, you need _____.

20. To clean up leaves, you need _____.

I.E.P. Goal: The student will identify items needed in common situations with 90% or greater accuracy.

Finish each sentence.

21. To wash your hair, you need _____.

22. To see better, you need _____.

23. To ride to school, you need _____.

24. To buy your lunch, you need _____.

25. To get well, you need _____.

26. To eat ice cream, you need _____.

27. To ride on the water, you need _____.

28. To protect your feet in the snow, you need _____.

29. To make your drink cold, you need _____.

30. To hold up your pants, you need _____.

31. To blow your nose, you need _____.

32. To catch a fish, you need _____.

33. To climb to the roof, you need _____.

34. To fly a kite, you need _____.

35. To tie your shoe, you need _____.

36. To light a fire, you need _____.

37. To splash, you need _____.

38. To mow the lawn, you need _____.

39. To feed a newborn baby, you need _____.

40. To keep dry in a storm, you need _____.

I.E.P. Goal: The student will identify items needed in common situations with 90% or greater accuracy.

Self-Expression

Name _____

Finish each sentence.

41. To slice bread, you need _____.

42. To mail a postcard, you need _____.

43. To get up on time, you need _____.

44. To water the lawn, you need _____.

45. To play hopscotch, you need _____.

46. To pack your clothes, you need _____.

47. To grow flowers, you need _____.

48. To weigh apples, you need _____.

49. To get rid of pencil marks, you need _____.

50. To slide down a hill in the snow, you need _____.

51. To keep from burning your hands when you take something from the oven, you

   need _____.

52. To turn the light on and off, you need _____.

53. To stop your bicycle, you need _____.

54. To find which way is north, you need _____.

55. To keep juice from spilling out of a bottle, you need _____.

56. To hold a stack of cards together, you need _____.

57. To play a drum, you need _____.

58. To scoop fish out of a tank, you need _____.

59. To make a puppet move, you need _____.

60. To make the car turn the corner, you need _____.

I.E.P. Goal: The student will identify items needed in common situations with 90% or greater accuracy.

Self-Expression   181

Name _____

Answer *yes* or *no* to each question.   The first one is done for you.

1. If someone is unhappy, is she happy?   yes   (no)

2. If someone moves slowly, is he quick?   yes   no

3. If someone is starved, is she hungry?   yes   no

4. If someone is happy, is she sad?   yes   no

5. If someone is nice, is she mean?   yes   no

6. If someone is afraid, is he scared?   yes   no

7. If someone has a fever, is she sick?   yes   no

8. If someone is angry, is he mad?   yes   no

9. If someone is skinny, is she thin?   yes   no

10. If someone is tall, is he short?   yes   no

11. If someone is sleepy, is she tired?   yes   no

12. If someone is cute, is he nice looking?   yes   no

13. If someone is cheerful, is he happy?   yes   no

14. If someone is frightened, is she afraid?   yes   no

15. If someone is quick, is he fast?   yes   no

16. If someone is chilly, is she hot?   yes   no

17. If someone is laughing, is he upset?   yes   no

18. If someone is kind, is she nice?   yes   no

19. If someone is hidden, is she easily seen?   yes   no

20. If someone is silly, is he funny?   yes   no

I.E.P. Goal: The student will answer yes *or* no *to descriptive questions about people with 90% or greater accuracy.*

Self-Expression   182

Answer *yes* or *no* to each question.

21.	If someone is talkative, is he quiet?	yes	no
22.	If someone is grumpy, is she happy?	yes	no
23.	If someone is bright, is she smart?	yes	no
24.	If someone is mistaken, is he wrong?	yes	no
25.	If someone is pleased, is she happy?	yes	no
26.	If someone is rowdy, is she loud?	yes	no
27.	If someone is confused, is he sure?	yes	no
28.	If someone is drowsy, is he sleepy?	yes	no
29.	If someone is shy, is she quiet?	yes	no
30.	If someone is troubled, is she worried?	yes	no
31.	If someone is unhappy, is he joyful?	yes	no
32.	If someone is healthy, is she sick?	yes	no
33.	If someone is worried, is he cheerful?	yes	no
34.	If someone is nice, is she nasty?	yes	no
35.	If someone is tearful, is he upset?	yes	no
36.	If someone is surprised, is she amazed?	yes	no
37.	If someone is enjoying himself, is he bored?	yes	no
38.	If someone is bothered, is she upset?	yes	no
39.	If someone follows the rules, is she obedient?	yes	no
40.	If someone is late, is he tardy?	yes	no

I.E.P. Goal: The student will answer yes *or* no *to descriptive questions about people with 90% or greater accuracy.*

Read each sentence.   Then, match each feeling word to the sentence that describes the feeling. The first one is done for you.

1. _c_ Dan should have been home an hour ago.   a. happy

  _b_ I can't have a puppy.   b. sad

  _a_ This is the best present I've ever had.   c. worried

2. ____ A party?   For me?   a. angry

  ____ Don't ever come back!   b. surprised

  ____ I'll miss you.   c. unhappy

3. ____ It's awfully dark down there.   a. scared

  ____ I get to go to the circus!   b. glad

  ____ She has more pencils than I.   c. jealous

4. ____ I won the spelling bee.   a. frightened

  ____ Mark heard a voice outside.   b. sorry

  ____ I didn't mean to do it.   c. proud

5. ____ She didn't ask me to the party.   a. unafraid

  ____ I sleep with the light turned off.   b. hurt

  ____ Jan made the team.   c. glad

6. ____ I'm home all by myself.   a. furious

  ____ Pam gave her scarf to me.   b. lonely

  ____ My baby brother ripped up my new book. c. grateful

7. ____ No, I won't share that with you.   a. excited

  ____ Did you see the surprise?   b. disappointed

  ____ The ice-cream truck didn't come today. c. selfish

8. ____ I have the prettiest hair in school.   a. conceited

  ____ Stop touching my teddy bear!   b. cheerful

  ____ Isn't it nice outside today?   c. grumpy

I.E.P. Goal: The student will infer feelings from statements with 90% or greater accuracy.

Name _____

Read each sentence.   Then, match each feeling word to the sentence that describes the feeling.

9. ____ You can sit with me.   a. shy

  ____ Quit spraying me with water!   b. nice

  ____ I don't want to sing in front of the family.   c. annoyed

10. ____ Let me help you carry your books.   a. rude

  ____ Don't bother me!   b. pleasant

  ____ Oh boy!   We get to go outside today.   c. glad

11. ____ That's not fair.   I was here first!   a. nervous

  ____ I could fall asleep right here.   b. mad

  ____ Fred doesn't like getting on the stage.   c. weary

12. ____ I am so lucky.   a. guilty

  ____ We don't want him on our team.   b. dislike

  ____ I ate the cheese we were saving for lunch.   c. thankful

13. ____ I hope that dog doesn't chase us.   a. embarrassed

  ____ I fell right in front of the principal.   b. honest

  ____ You gave me too much change.   c. fearful

14. ____ No matter how hard I try, I can't win.   a. frustrated

  ____ Mary Ann was very mean to me.   b. upset

  ____ Oh no!   You left the stove on all night?   c. alarmed

15. ____ I got all of the problems right!   a. puzzled

  ____ She shouldn't talk to me that way.   b. pleased

  ____ How does this piece fit on the toy train?   c. resentful

16. ____ Nobody cares about me.   a. relieved

  ____ I didn't lose it after all!   b. moody

  ____ My picture was voted the best.   c. honored

I.E.P. Goal: The student will infer feelings from statements with 90% or greater accuracy.

 **Lesson 5**

Name _____

Read each statement.   Then, match the feeling to the action.   The first one is done for you.

1. Dawn got a new hair ribbon.   She is . . .

   sad   angry   (happy)

2. Harry covered his head with a pillow during the storm.   He was . . .

   scared   hurt   glad

3. Bart's umbrella fell apart when he opened it.   He was . . .

   joyful   surprised   thrilled

4. The little boy couldn't find his lunch money.   He was . . .

   worried   selfish   happy

5. The huge dog chased after Billy.   Billy was . . .

   cheerful   proud   afraid

6. Tomorrow, we're going on a field trip to the zoo.   We are . . .

   grumpy   excited   helpless

7. Tanya thinks she got an "A" on her test.   She is . . .

   hopeful   frightened   honest

8. Dave can't remember if the house was on the left or on the right.   He is . . .

   hurt   confused   dishonest

9. The baby-sitter always takes us to the park.   She is . . .

   nice   gloomy   alarmed

10. Mrs. Rios has been sick three days.   Her students are . . .

    guilty   concerned   honest

I.E.P. Goal: The student will infer feelings from actions with 90% or greater accuracy.

Self-Expression   186

Read each statement.   Then, match the feeling to the action.

11. Sue makes everyone feel better with her smile.   She is . . .

cheerful   angry   frustrated

12. I am sorry your dog ran away.   I am . . .

conceited   fearful   sympathetic

13. Nathan threw his books on the floor.   He is . . .

grumpy   flattered   proud

14. Janice won an award for perfect attendance.   She is . . .

depressed   proud   nervous

15. Missy forgot to invite her cousin, Jeff, to her party.   Jeff is . . .

nasty   charming   hurt

16. Scott won't share with anyone.   He is . . .

generous   relieved   selfish

17. At the fair, Aaron won ten free tickets.   He was . . .

selfish   surprised   humiliated

18. The teacher mistakenly thought Leslie was a girl.   He was . . .

embarrassed   thrilled   appreciative

19. The bell rang before Brooke could give her speech.   She was . . .

conceited   relieved   lonely

20. Ned caught a terrible cold.   He is . . .

thankful   overjoyed   miserable

I.E.P. Goal: The student will infer feelings from actions with 90% or greater accuracy.

Lesson 6

Describe how you think each person would feel in the situations below. The first one is done for you.

_____lonely_____   1. Don's best friend moved to another city. How do you think Don feels?

_____   2. Your sister took your bookbag and hid it from you. How do you think you would feel?

_____   3. It's Paula's first day at school. Her teacher gives her a big hug and smile and tells her everything will be fine. How do you think Paula feels about her teacher?

_____   4. The first grade boys' basketball team was given front row seats to watch a famous basketball player. How do you think they felt?

_____   5. You studied extra hard for your spelling test. You were the only one to get a 100. How would that make you feel?

_____   6. Danny accidentally knocked over his glass and milk spilled all over the floor. He told his mom and began to cry. How do you think Danny felt?

_____   7. You picked out the perfect birthday gift for your mom. But, when you went to get it, they had all been sold. How would you feel?

_____   8. Hal ran after Allen, who was kicking rocks on the sidewalk. When Hal asked if he wanted to play, Allen said, "Go away and leave me alone!" How do you think Allen was feeling?

_____   9. Angela was showing her parents a new trick on the swing set. Her hand slipped and she fell face first in the mud. How do you think Angela felt?

_____   10. The bus was getting ready to leave school, but your brother wasn't on it yet. How would you feel?

_____   11. The kids were watching a movie when suddenly the lights went out. The wind began howling outside. Strange, creaky noises seemed to be coming from the attic. How do you think the kids felt?

I.E.P. Goal: The student will identify feelings in given situations with 90% or greater accuracy.

Self-Expression   188

Name _____

Describe how you think each person would feel in the situations below.

_____ 12. The class was reading out loud. Marcie was daydreaming. When the teacher called on her, Marcie didn't know where they were on the page. Joan quietly pointed out the sentence to her without the teacher knowing. How do you think Marcie felt about Joan?

_____ 13. Someone accidentally let Eddie's pet bunny out of his cage and he ran away. Pete told Eddie that he knew how he felt because he lost his pet bird the same way last year. How do you think Pete felt?

_____ 14. Our neighbor always has a smile on his face. No matter what happens, he never seems to get angry or lose his temper. Just being around him makes you laugh. How do you think our neighbor feels?

_____ 15. The police officer came home after working all night and most of the day. She walked slowly up the steps and stretched out in the chair on the porch. She was asleep in only a few seconds. How do you think the police officer felt?

_____ 16. Last night was the first time Jenny danced onstage in front of everyone in the school. Before, she had only danced for her parents and her brother. How do you think Jenny felt?

_____ 17. When Andy started his homework, he couldn't remember if he was supposed to read page 13 in his reading book or do page 13 in his math book. How do you think Andy felt?

_____ 18. Sarah had just moved to a new school where she didn't know anyone. At lunch, she was separated from her class and had to sit at a table by herself. How do you think Sarah felt?

_____ 19. The principal came into the classroom and asked if anyone knew about the broken window. Ann sank down in her chair, since she was the one who threw the baseball that broke the window. How do you think Ann was feeling?

_____ 20. Jon spent hours learning how to kick the ball through the goalposts. But it seemed the more he practiced, the worse he got. How do you think Jon felt?

I.E.P. Goal: The student will identify feelings in given situations with 90% or greater accuracy.

Self-Expression

Name _____

Complete each statement.   Explain your answer.   The first one is done for you.

1. You should take a bath every day so *you will be clean*   .

2. You should eat your breakfast every morning so _____.

3. You should go to the doctor when you're sick so _____.

4. You shouldn't touch the top of the stove because _____.

5. You should go to the bus stop on time so _____.

6. You should put ice cream in the freezer so _____.

7. You should tie your shoelaces so _____.

8. You should tell your mom where you are so _____.

9. You should wear boots in the snow so _____.

10. You should water your flowers so _____.

11. You should come in when it's raining so _____.

12. You shouldn't wander away from your mother in the store because _____.

13. You should send someone a birthday card because _____.

14. You should put the top on the glue so _____.

15. You should study your spelling words so _____.

16. You should be quiet in a library so _____.

17. You should take notes when you're in class so _____.

18. You shouldn't touch a fallen electrical wire because _____.

19. You shouldn't drink out of bottles kept under the sink because _____.

20. You should put the shower curtain inside the tub so _____.

I.E.P. Goal: The student will give reasons for common actions with 90% or greater accuracy.

Self-Expression   190

Lesson 8

Name _____

Tell how you feel about each statement.   Explain your reason.

1. Dogs should be allowed in school.	yes	no	not sure
2. No one should have to get a haircut.	yes	no	not sure
3. You should brush your teeth once each hour.	yes	no	not sure
4. Kids should watch TV whenever they want.	yes	no	not sure
5. Schools shouldn't have grades.	yes	no	not sure
6. Everyone should eat an apple every day.	yes	no	not sure
7. Seat belts should be put in school buses.	yes	no	not sure
8. All blankets should be red.	yes	no	not sure
9. It should snow at least 10 days a year.	yes	no	not sure
10. Every child should have a pet.	yes	no	not sure
11. People should wear sunglasses all the time.	yes	no	not sure
12. School should be cancelled on Mondays.	yes	no	not sure
13. Kids should be allowed to drive cars.	yes	no	not sure
14. We should have summer weather all year round.	yes	no	not sure
15. You should always tell the truth.	yes	no	not sure
16. Kids shouldn't have to eat vegetables.	yes	no	not sure
17. Tennis shoes cost too much.	yes	no	not sure
18. You should work math problems with a pen.	yes	no	not sure
19. Boys and girls should be in separate classes.	yes	no	not sure
20. The cafeteria should serve pizza every day.	yes	no	not sure

I.E.P. Goal: The student will express personal opinions about statements with 90% or greater accuracy.

ANSWER KEY

Question Comprehension

Lesson 1   pages 8-10

1. yes
2. no
3. yes
4. yes
5. no
6. yes
7. yes
8. no
9. no
10. no
11. yes
12. no
13. yes
14. yes
15. no
16. yes
17. yes
18. no
19. no
20. no
21. yes
22. no
23. no
24. no
25. yes
26. yes
27. no
28. no
29. yes
30. yes
31. no
32. yes
33. no
34. no
35. no
36. yes
37. no
38. no
39. yes
40. yes
41. yes
42. no
43. yes
44. yes
45. no
46. yes
47. no
48. no
49. no
50. no
51. yes
52. no
53. no
54. no
55. no
56. yes
57. no
58. yes
59. yes
60. yes

Lesson 2   pages 11-13

1. yes
2. yes
3. yes
4. yes
5. no
6. no
7. no
8. yes
9. no
10. no
11. no
12. no
13. no
14. yes
15. no
16. yes
17. yes
18. no
19. yes
20. no
21. yes
22. yes
23. yes
24. no
25. no
26. no
27. no
28. yes
29. no
30. no
31. yes
32. no
33. no
34. yes
35. yes
36. yes
37. yes
38. no
39. yes
40. no
41. no
42. no
43. yes
44. no
45. yes
46. yes
47. yes
48. yes
49. no
50. no
51. yes
52. no
53. no
54. yes
55. no
56. yes
57. no
58. no
59. no
60. yes

Lesson 3   pages 14-15

1. yes
2. yes
3. no
4. yes
5. yes
6. yes
7. yes
8. no
9. yes
10. no
11. yes
12. yes
13. no
14. yes
15. no
16. no
17. yes
18. no
19. yes
20. no
21. no
22. no
23. no
24. no
25. yes
26. no
27. no
28. yes
29. yes
30. yes
31. yes
32. yes
33. no
34. yes
35. yes
36. yes
37. yes
38. no
39. no
40. yes

Lesson 4   pages 16-17

1. no
2. yes
3. yes
4. no
5. no
6. yes
7. yes
8. yes
9. no
10. yes
11. no
12. no
13. yes
14. no
15. no
16. no
17. no
18. no
19. yes
20. yes
21. yes
22. no
23. no
24. no
25. no
26. no
27. no
28. yes
29. yes
30. yes
31. yes
32. yes
33. no
34. yes
35. yes
36. yes
37. yes
38. no
39. yes
40. yes
41. yes
42. yes
43. no
44. yes
45. no
46. yes
47. no
48. yes
49. yes
50. yes
51. yes
52. no
53. yes
54. no
55. no
56. yes
57. yes
58. no
59. no
60. yes
61. no
62. no
63. no
64. yes
65. yes
66. yes
67. no
68. yes
69. no
70. no
71. no
72. no
73. yes
74. no
75. yes
76. yes
77. no
78. no
79. yes
80. yes

Lesson 5   pages 18-19

1. no
2. yes
3. yes
4. no
5. yes
6. yes
7. no
8. no
9. yes
10. no
11. no
12. yes
13. yes
14. yes
15. yes
16. no
17. no
18. no
19. no
20. no
21. no
22. no
23. yes
24. no
25. no
26. no
27. no
28. yes
29. no
30. no
31. yes
32. yes
33. no
34. yes
35. no
36. no
37. yes

38. yes
39. yes
40. no

Lesson 6   **pages 20-21**

1. All
2. Some
3. Some
4. Some
5. Some
6. All
7. All
8. Some
9. All
10. All
11. All
12. Some
13. Some
14. All
15. Some
16. Some
17. All
18. Some
19. Some
20. All
21. All
22. Some
23. Some
24. All
25. Some
26. All
27. Some
28. Some
29. All
30. Some
31. All
32. Some
33. Some
34. All
35. Some
36. All
37. All
38. Some
39. Some
40. Some
41. Some
42. Some
43. Some
44. Some
45. Some
46. Some
47. All
48. All
49. Some
50. Some
51. All
52. Some
53. Some
54. All
55. Some
56. All
57. Some
58. Some
59. All
60. All
61. Some
62. All
63. Some
64. All
65. Some
66. All
67. Some

68. All
69. All
70. Some
71. Some
72. Some
73. Some
74. Some
75. All
76. All
77. All
78. Some
79. All
80. Some

Lesson 7   **pages 22-23**

1. true
2. false
3. true
4. false
5. false
6. false
7. true
8. true
9. true
10. false
11. true
12. false
13. false
14. true
15. false
16. true
17. true
18. false
19. false
20. true
21. true
22. false
23. false
24. false
25. true
26. true
27. false
28. false
29. false
30. true
31. false
32. true
33. false
34. true
35. true
36. true
37. false
38. true
39. false
40. false

Lesson 8   **pages 24-26**

1. always
2. never
3. never
4. sometimes
5. sometimes
6. always
7. sometimes
8. always
9. sometimes
10. sometimes
11. sometimes
12. always
13. never
14. never
15. sometimes

16. never
17. sometimes
18. sometimes
19. sometimes
20. always
21. sometimes
22. never
23. always
24. never
25. always
26. never
27. sometimes
28. always
29. never
30. always
31. never
32. always
33. never
34. sometimes
35. never
36. sometimes
37. never
38. sometimes
39. always
40. never
41. sometimes
42. never
43. never
44. sometimes
45. always
46. never
47. always
48. never
49. sometimes
50. always
51. always
52. sometimes
53. always
54. never
55. always
56. always
57. never
58. always
59. always
60. never

Association

Lesson 1   **pages 28-29**

1. eat something
2. wash them
3. answer it
4. change them
5. make another piece, scrap it off
6. it's time to start school, time to go home
7. pick it up and sew it back on
8. give it to the teacher, find who lost it
9. pick it up, do it over, it will be ruined
10. sharpen it, use a different pencil
11. it will melt
12. call home, borrow some, try to find it
13. close the window
14. it will be hard in the morning
15. put some air in it
16. it will break
17. they win

18. it might fall out
19. you might burn your tongue
20. it might go to the bathroom on the floor
21. ask someone to take it out
22. open it
23. you will be 10 on your next birthday
24. you'll swallow water and choke
25. it will be the other team's turn at bat
26. it might die
27. tomorrow is Saturday
28. we go to school
29. you will be tired
30. it might overflow
31. you can't peddle it, get it fixed
32. it will pop
33. go inside right away
34. stop and look both ways before going
35. the batteries are getting weak
36. your hair will be sticky
37. the balloon will stick to the wall
38. you won't get well

Lesson 2   **pages 30-31**

1. he might fall
2. the tower might fall
3. the wave might wash away the castle
4. the cat knocked over the flower pot
5. he took your picture
6. the baby may put the marbles in her mouth
7. the popcorn burned
8. the Lings were moving
9. Joleen was having a birthday party
10. the ice cream will melt
11. someone knocked a jar off the shelf
12. the man hit his head on the doorway
13. the person who called hung up
14. they were taking a test
15. his books were overdue and he owed a fine
16. it shrunk
17. the boy delivered the newspaper
18. a parade was about to begin
19. soda sprayed all over the kitchen
20. Beth had a date to a special dance
21. a fire drill
22. the man was going home
23. the restaurant forgot to put cheese on the sandwich
24. they used all their bait and didn't catch anything
25. the film broke and they were fixing it

Lesson 3   **page 32**

1. same: you can eat both

ANSWER KEY

different: apples are red, oranges are orange

2. same: four legs; farm animals
different: cows give milk; we ride horses

3. same: used to write; are thin and long
different: pens have ink, pencils have lead

4. same: both have a motor; need gasoline
different: motorcycle has two wheels, car has four

5. same: foods; eaten in bowls with spoons
different: cereal can be eaten dry

6. same: long; can wear both
different: belt has buckle and holes; ribbon can be worn in hair

7. same: young; both cry; need to be watched carefully
different: babies are humans, puppies are dogs; babies learn to talk, puppies learn to bark

8. same: long, thin metal objects
different: knife found in kitchen, screwdriver found in tool box

9. same: made of cloth; rectangular
different: towel is used to dry off, blanket is used for warmth; blanket is bigger

10. same: both clean us; used in bathroom
different: shampoo is used on hair, soap is used on body

11. same: found at carnival; fun to ride; go in circles
different: merry go round has horses; Ferris wheel sits upright

12. same: soft; desserts; eaten with spoons
different: ice cream is frozen; ice cream melts

13. same: both have long handles; used to clean up
different: brooms are used on floors, rakes are used on yards; most rakes are metal

14. same: sticky; used to hold things together
different: tape is on roll, glue comes in a bottle

15. same: desserts; baked
different: pies have a crust; cakes have frosting

16. same: keep us warm; have sleeves
different: bathrobe worn in house, coat worn outside

17. same: eaten with something else
different: ketchup is red, mayonnaise is white

18. same: are used with brushes; comes in many colors

different: paint used on paper and houses, nail polish on fingernails

19. same: flowers; have petals, stems and leaves
different: different shapes; roses have thorns

20. same: bodies of water; both have fish
different: oceans are larger; oceans are salt water, lakes are fresh water

21. same: both are animals; have tails
different: skunks smell bad; squirrels live in trees

22. same: made of paper; can be torn
different: envelops are smaller; envelops hold letters

23. same: both are toys; have faces
different: can put hand inside puppet; can change a doll's clothes

24. same: go from one floor to another; need electricity
different: elevators have doors that close and buttons to push

25. same: round with hole in the center; eaten for breakfast
different: doughnuts are sweeter; bagels are toasted

26. same: both are read; printed on paper
different: newspapers are published everyday, magazines usually once a month; magazines are stapled or glued, newspapers are folded

27. same: both are still; both show people or animals
different: a photograph is flat, a statue has a front, back, and sides; statues are chiseled from stone, photographs are taken with film

28. same: both show land and water locations; both are colored; both show names of places
different: globes are round, maps are flat; maps are used in the car

29. same: both go around your wrist; both can be made of metal
different: handcuffs need a key to unlock

30. same: both are small metal objects; both hold papers together
different: staples go through paper

31. same: both are jungle animals; both have four legs and a long tail
different: leopards are spotted; lions have a mane

32. same: both are used in offices and schools; both have keyboards
different: computers can be used to play games; computers are more expensive

33. same: both are used to hit a ball across a net; both have handles
different: tennis rackets have long handles, Ping-Pong paddles have short handles; tennis rackets have strings, Ping-Pong paddles are solid

34. same: people stay overnight in both; they each have lots of beds
different: jails have cells, hotels have rooms; people stay in a hotel because they want to

35. same: both make rules; both try to be fair; both give out punishment
different: judge works in a courtroom; judge works with people in court, parents work with children at home

36. same: both are shaped like cubes and can be stacked
different: dice have dots or numbers on them; babies play with blocks not dice; dice are smaller

37. same: both are types of dogs; have four legs, ears and tails
different: dalmatians are spotted; poodles have curly hair; firemen have dalmatians at the fire station

38. same: both hop; are amphibians; lay eggs
different: toads have dry rough skin, frogs are smooth; frogs live in water, toads live on land

Lesson 4   pages 33-34

1. zipper
2. stove
3. kite, airplane
4. rabbit, kangaroo
5. mouth, tongue
6. nose, flowers
7. hands, fingers
8. ears
9. shovel
10. crayons, markers
11. plants, people
12. horn, alarm, pager
13. wind, horn
14. teeth, a cow
15. hair, ribbon
16. car, runner
17. clock
18. pen, pencil
19. squirt gun, citrus fruit
20. an eye, a light

21. knife
22. tooth, stomach, feet
23. car, music, movie, school
24. door, window
25. water, soup
26. mosquito, teeth, dog
27. paper
28. broom
29. hose, spray bottle
30. water, paint
31. toilet
32. glass, toys
33. mouse, door
34. lights, lightning
35. bells, keys, coins
36. car, bike, clock
37. pencils, crayons, markers
38. shoelaces, ribbon necktie
39. spoon, a cook
40. heart, drum
41. hands
42. baseball player, swing
43. leaves, rain, kids
44. Jell-O, earthquakes
45. stove, microwave
46. sugar, honey
47. ice, refrigerator
48. eyes
49. snakes, cats
50. lava, water
51. glass, plastic, ice
52. tongue
53. hot stove, fire
54. tape recorder
55. scale
56. flowers
57. mosquito bite
58. dog
59. police, parents
60. ice cream
61. soda pop
62. blanket, lid, clothes
63. raw vegetables, cereal
64. horse
65. air conditioner refrigerator, ice
66. weather, seasons, people
67. scary movies, people, animals
68. movie, story, rain
69. ruler, yardstick, cup
70. button, snap, paper clip
71. bathtub, sink
72. bacon, grease
73. horse
74. singer, movie
75. milk
76. colors, cloth, jeans
77. paint, banana, sunburned skin
78. pipe
79. electricity
80. balloon

Lesson 5   pages 35-36

1. writes
2. keeps a baby's shirt clean
3. makes hair neat
4. keep hands warm
5. cleans teeth
6. heats, cooks food
7. beeps, makes noise
8. sticks things together
9. covers, keeps us warm
10. sweeps

ANSWER KEY

11. opens a lock
12. pounds
13. help someone see
14. tells time, ticks
15. shines, warms us
16. flies
17. cuts
18. digs
19. keeps food cold
20. holds things, opens and shuts
21. fastens clothes
22. shines, helps us see
23. covers a cut
24. provides music and news
25. smell
26. keep feet dry and warm
27. holds clothes in a closet
28. plays music
29. measures
30. blows
31. cools
32. grows, provides shade
33. holds wood together
34. tells dates
35. wails to warn us
36. keeps drinks hot or cold
37. keeps a dog from running away
38. keeps cook from burning hands
39. keeps insects away
40. puts out fires

Lesson 6   pages 37-42
Comparison of Two Items
1. ant, cup, earring, book, slice of bread
2. butterfly, peacock, bouquet of flowers, shiny car, new dress
3. heater, summer, toaster, popcorn, soup
4. piece of paper, sock, newspaper, sponge, dollar bill
5. grandmother, father, mother, cat, cow
6. turtle, bicycle, skipping, boat, bus
7. scissors, knife, axe, shovel, toothpick
8. apple, cookie, chocolate bar, cake, chewing gum
9. day, minute, year, month, morning
10. towel, sidewalk, paper towel, alligator's back, pine cone
11. bulldozer
12. new shoes
13. piece of foil
14. thirty-year-old woman
15. marshmallows
16. grape
17. couch
18. pretzel stick
19. nachos
20. paper bag
21. pickle
22. cotton ball
23. sidewalk at noon
24. lunch box
25. flashlight

26. rabbit
27. rainstorm
28. make a quilt
29. tomato
30. tying your shoe with one hand

Comparison of Three Items
1. racehorse
2. soap
3. writing
4. dish
5. kitten
6. whale
7. cereal
8. noise in the dark
9. briefcase
10. detergent
11. Ping-Pong ball
12. yardstick
13. pajamas
14. plant
15. playing cards
16. icy sidewalk
17. jokes
18. sponge

Comparison of Items Using Judgment
1. five-dollar bill
2. a child at the beach
3. chocolate syrup
4. guitar
5. play cards
6. sweater and pants
7. pencil case
8. television show
9. museum
10. crossing a busy highway
11. covered wagon
12. cookie
13. skateboard
14. paint set
15. novel
16. stuffed bear
17. bookstore
18. butcher shop
19. ice cream
20. "Don't Walk" sign

Lesson 7   pages 43-44
1. towel
2. cup
3. carrot
4. banana
5. desks
6. feathers
7. diapers
8. doorknob
9. sugar
10. birthday cake
11. shower
12. key
13. chewing gum
14. bus
15. stairs
16. pillow
17. cone
18. stamp
19. handlebars
20. barn
21. baby-sitter
22. shoelaces

23. ink
24. eyelashes
25. elbow
26. rake
27. students
28. grandmother
29. uncle
30. noon
31. beaver
32. crust
33. fountain
34. Band-Aid, bandage
35. paddle, oar
36. crutch
37. globe
38. cradle
39. quilt
40. judge

Lesson 8   pages 45-47
1. soft
2. red
3. hearing
4. painting
5. bedroom
6. moon
7. cutting
8. dig
9. pool, lake
10. gloves, mittens
11. necktie, necklace
12. cage, birdhouse, nest
13. straight
14. round
15. colt
16. doorknob
17. vacuum cleaner, sweeper
18. question
19. sweet
20. shoes
21. money
22. three
23. rings
24. stamps
25. juicy
26. hoses
27. dark
28. sticks
29. fruit, grapes
30. office, hospital
31. ink
32. box
33. home runs
34. tame
35. hoots
36. lid
37. classes, subjects
38. court
39. cars
40. frame
41. rink
42. snow
43. hand
44. loud
45. push
46. math, accounting
47. feet
48. flavor
49. soft
50. door, gate
51. teeth
52. house, letter

53. fish, frog
54. dog, wolf
55. potato
56. find
57. throw
58. pillow
59. public
60. street

Specific Word Finding

Lesson 1   pages 49-50
1. cut
2. eat, fix, bring
3. drink, make, pass
4. mow, trim
5. feed, hold, rock
6. draw, drive, get
7. kick, throw, catch
8. color
9. slide, go
10. push, get in
11. walk, pat, feed
12. open, close
13. wash, put away
14. clean, go to
15. water, smell
16. swing, play
17. read, buy, look at
18. brush, floss
19. ride, fly
20. ride
21. sit
22. take
23. send
24. pick up, read
25. watch, win, enjoy
26. light, blow out
27. roll, pick up
28. cut, file, paint
29. put, glue
30. paint, draw, hang
31. step on, sit on
32. go to, call
33. buy, open, wrap
34. bake, cook, put it
35. save, spend
36. climb, cut down
37. watch, go to
38. make, sleep in
39. slide, roll, fall
40. write, draw
41. tell, look at
42. cook, eat
43. pat
44. break, cook
45. blow, wipe
46. play, dig
47. throw, catch
48. ring, push
49. peel, eat
50. play
51. beat, play
52. do, wash
53. wear
54. fish, swim
55. pack, carry
56. shovel
57. slice, pick, eat
58. kick
59. load, unload
60. wear

196

61. cut, saw
62. jump
63. sit, lie, sunbathe
64. check out, borrow
65. erase, write on
66. read, look at
67. look
68. sing
69. wear, buy, knit
70. wait, stand
71. go, listen
72. squeeze
73. stand
74. aim, shoot
75. fill
76. chop, cut
77. sweep
78. write, think of
79. choose, pick, get
80. make, break

Lesson 2   pages 51-54

1. mittens, boots
2. cereal
3. cake, candy
4. ice cream
5. medicine
6. dog food, cat food
7. flour, sugar
8. books
9. milk, orange juice
10. cookies
11. milk, formula
12. cake, pie
13. lemonade, water
14. bread
15. soup, stew
16. lettuce, cabbage
17. jeans, shoes
18. toast, fruit
19. chips, pretzels
20. cereal, doughnuts
21. cards
22. chalk
23. corn, green beans
24. soap
25. clothes
26. dirt
27. meat, vegetables
28. popcorn
29. clothes
30. detergent, soap
31. food
32. butter
33. toothpaste
34. gasoline
35. toys
36. rain
37. crayons
38. grapes, bananas
39. yarn
40. chocolate chips
41. doughnuts
42. hot dogs, buns
43. milk
44. skis, boots
45. paint
46. books
47. leaves
48. thread
49. oil
50. meat

51. stairs
52. snow
53. money
54. oars
55. paint, glue
56. salt, pepper
57. students, kids
58. groceries, food
59. corn, wheat
60. film
61. trees
62. fabric, material
63. dishes, glasses
64. fish, water
65. slippers
66. bricks
67. nails
68. teeth
69. oxygen, air
70. hay
71. crutches
72. sand, water
73. pictures
74. medicine
75. coffee, root beer
76. patients, chairs
77. tigers, lions
78. drawers
79. geese, sheep
80. wood

Lesson 3   pages 55-56

1. Minnie Mouse
2. toothpaste
3. cake, cookies
4. brush
5. socks
6. cheese
7. lock
8. chair
9. knife, spoon
10. Ernie
11. ball
12. crayons
13. girls
14. down
15. boys, women
16. pans
17. go, get it
18. saucer
19. cats
20. shovel
21. nails
22. trucks
23. go
24. shut
25. mouth
26. coat
27. film
28. hat
29. dryer
30. gentlemen
31. dirty
32. bows
33. listen, see
34. grandpa
35. washcloth
36. butter
37. paper
38. moon, stars
39. shoes
40. dried, paste

41. sister
42. little
43. no
44. pencil, crayons
45. thunder
46. nurse
47. queen
48. back
49. day
50. white
51. Jill
52. see, smell
53. a hard place, roll
54. the Beast
55. right
56. cut
57. right
58. coffee, cookies
59. vanilla
60. vegetables
61. false
62. roll
63. limes
64. leg
65. ketchup
66. needles
67. crayons, paper
68. buns
69. plastic
70. blankets
71. bolts
72. south
73. state, county
74. cold
75. pop
76. subtract
77. miss
78. vinegar
79. paint
80. thread

Lesson 4   pages 57-58

1. picture
2. chair
3. bed, cot
4. car, bowl
5. food, candy
6. song
7. milk, juice
8. door
9. teacher, pictures
10. fish, thief
11. paper, cake
12. best
13. cat, dog
14. shoes, laces
15. zoo, store, mall
16. man, woman
17. dog
18. breakfast, dinner
19. picture
20. broken toy, food
21. music
22. story
23. trampoline, bed
24. money, allowance
25. cake, cookies
26. vacation, trip
27. sky, TV
28. banana peel
29. medicine, test
30. bread, cookies

31. wallet, penny
32. table, chair
33. present, speech
34. package, letter
35. story, letter
36. picture
37. eggs
38. clothes, dishes
39. comedian, clown
40. grass, bushes
41. game, prize
42. money, kids, cars
43. numbers
44. children, class
45. food, flowers
46. flowers, seeds
47. door, window
48. button, door
49. door, window
50. piano, game
51. leftovers, candy
52. helicopter, kite
53. balloon, popcorn
54. car, truck
55. operator, police
56. fort, building
57. vegetables
58. music, bells
59. grocery cart, bowl
60. parade, cheer
61. TV, necklace, car
62. house, car, room
63. car, house, food
64. food, drinks
65. papers, rocks
66. baby, books
67. party, store
68. corner
69. bills, rent
70. neighbors
71. curtain, box
72. book
73. ice
74. leaves, grass
75. room, paper
76. box, cat, apples
77. money, food
78. teacher
79. party, game
80. president, mayor

Lesson 5   pages 59-60

1. hands
2. book
3. race, prize
4. teeth, hair
5. lawn, grass
6. bed, sleeping bag
7. scissors
8. lake, water
9. ladder
10. floor
11. feet
12. babies
13. oven
14. team
15. medicine
16. closet
17. light
18. train, bus
19. chain saw, saw
20. bikes

ANSWER KEY

21. window, door
22. fence
23. letter
24. homework
25. pool, lake, ocean
26. door
27. pencil
28. glasses
29. refrigerator
30. key
31. camera
32. hammer
33. clock, watch
34. table
35. milk
36. purse
37. cart, basket
38. airport
39. library
40. tent, sleeping bag

Lesson 6   pages 61-62

1. milk
2. bikes, ponies
3. chairs, bathtubs
4. chalkboards
5. bedroom
6. books, comics
7. hen, chicken, bird
8. telephone
9. shoes, socks
10. knife
11. umbrella, raincoat
12. library
13. kitchen
14. boats
15. trains
16. shovel
17. refrigerator
18. watch
19. towel
20. tissues, Kleenex
21. glasses
22. toothpaste, toothbrush
23. principal
24. fish
25. doctors, parents
26. carrots
27. ear
28. elephant
29. calendar
30. necklace
31. doorknob
32. bee
33. mailbox
34. bathtub
35. washcloth
36. cages
37. pilot
38. trees
39. collar
40. caterpillar

Lesson 7   pages 63-64

1. shoe, shoelaces
2. toothbrush, toothpaste, water
3. broom, dustpan
4. comb
5. crayons, markers, paper
6. spoon, bowl, soup
7. pajamas
8. book

9. trash can, garbage bag
10. water, soap, towels
11. spoon, bowl, box of cereal, milk
12. swimming suit, towel, pool/lake
13. money
14. shovel
15. bus/car
16. cheese, knife
17. wrapping paper, present, tape, ribbon
18. clock, mom/dad
19. curtains, shades
20. telephone, telephone number, 911
21. thermometer
22. milk, bottle, mom
23. pen/pencil, paper
24. dog food, dish
25. lawn mower
26. card, envelope, stamp, mailbox
27. peanut butter, bread, knife
28. sheets, pillowcases, blankets
29. hose, water, soap, bucket, sponge, towels
30. kite, string, wind
31. tissue/Kleenex
32. cocoa, cup, water/milk, stove, pan
33. hot dogs, buns, relishes
34. tree, axe, saw/chainsaw
35. watch, clock
36. scale
37. TV
38. rake, trash bags
39. suitcase, bag
40. radio, stereo, tapes, CDs, headphones
41. hose, faucet, sprinkler, water
42. key
43. sink, washing machine, water, soap
44. mitt, ball, hands
45. raincoat, hat, umbrella, boots
46. brownie mix, eggs, oil, pan, oven
47. flag, flagpole, rope
48. ticket, airplane, pilot
49. ladder, light bulb
50. raft, boat
51. ticket, movie theater
52. drum, drumsticks
53. pencil, paper, book, assignment
54. dictionary
55. snow, friends
56. ruler, wall
57. bricks, cement
58. doctor, cast, crutches
59. glue, tape
60. voice, words to the song, music
61. paper, pencil, calculator, memory
62. tape recorder, tape
63. telephone, number to call, operator, money
64. bat, ball, pitcher, baseball field
65. clothing store, dress you like, money

66. grocery store, list, cart, money
67. frosting, cake, knife
68. tweezers, needle, antiseptic
69. library, book, library card
70. water, cleanser, paper towels
71. vegetables, knife, bowl, dressing
72. fishing pole, line, hook, bait, net
73. grill, fuel, matches, steak
74. pliers, screw driver, directions
75. pan, turkey, oven
76. oar, paddle, boat
77. seeds, dirt, water, sun
78. ball, goal
79. food, park, blanket or table
80. ladder

Grammar

Lesson 1   page 66

1. I
2. She
3. You
4. He
5. She
6. It
7. It
8. You
9. We
10. They
11. He
12. We
13. We
14. She
15. We
16. I
17. You
18. She
19. I
20. They
21. You
22. They
23. They
24. He
25. You
26. We
27. It
28. He
29. I
30. They
31. I
32. It
33. He
34. They
35. It
36. He
37. She
38. I

Lesson 2   page 67

1. His
2. My
3. Your
4. Their
5. Our
6. My
7. His
8. Their
9. His
10. Her
11. Their

12. Our
13. Her
14. His
15. Our
16. My
17. Her
18. Our
19. Their
20. Your
21. My
22. Our
23. Their
24. His
25. her
26. our
27. his
28. my
29. her
30. your
31. you
32. my
33. his
34. her
35. their
36. his
37. her

Lesson 3   page 68

1. her
2. me
3. him
4. her
5. us
6. him
7. them
8. him
9. us
10. them
11. them
12. me
13. them
14. us
15. him
16. me
17. her
18. us
19. her
20. him
21. them
22. them
23. him
24. her
25. us
26. them
27. him
28. us
29. me
30. them
31. me
32. them
33. him
34. her, me
35. him, her

Lesson 4   pages 69-71

1. He
2. She
3. They
4. it
5. She
6. it
7. her

ANSWER KEY

8. They
9. him
10. He
11. He
12. him
13. It
14. She
15. He
16. She
17. It
18. He
19. They
20. It
21. him
22. He
23. They
24. She
25. He
26. They
27. We
28. them
29. They
30. They
31. We
32. They
33. us
34. them
35. them
36. it
37. them
38. him
39. her
40. her
41. them
42. We
43. her
44. us
45. him
46. them
47. us
48. We
49. We
50. Our
51. his
52. them
53. She, her
54. His, them
55. We, her
56. He, it
57. We, it
58. She, them
59. They, us
60. He, it, her

Lesson 5   pages 72-74

1. smaller
2. tallest
3. bigger
4. sicker
5. freshest
6. hottest
7. quietest
8. cheaper
9. littlest
10. funnier
11. friendliest
12. colder
13. faster
14. dirtiest
15. easier
16. crispier
17. softest

18. smallest
19. nicest
20. crunchiest
21. cleaner
22. sharper
23. rougher
24. richest
25. darker
26. most
27. heavier
28. prouder
29. busier
30. tastiest
31. angriest
32. lighter
33. messiest
34. tiniest
35. loudest
36. latest
37. lighter
38. best
39. narrower
40. ugliest
41. earlier
42. quicker
43. stickiest
44. rougher
45. older
46. shortest
47. skinniest
48. softer
49. neatest
50. better
51. shiniest
52. higher
53. sneakiest
54. spicier
55. more difficult
56. most honest
57. most ferocious
58. more nutritious
59. tighter
60. least

Lesson 6   pages 75-77

1. cans
2. boats
3. cats
4. spoons
5. coats
6. erasers
7. pennies
8. bicycles
9. doctors
10. ducks
11. carrots
12. beds
13. sisters
14. baskets
15. closets
16. tables
17. telephones
18. keys
19. rocks
20. brooms
21. nails
22. cameras
23. puppets
24. masks
25. bees
26. rulers
27. straws

28. whistles
29. bears
30. tractors
31. pumpkins
32. rabbits
33. drums
34. rooms
35. pockets
36. windows
37. notebooks
38. cavities
39. vans
40. helmets
41. canoes
42. batteries
43. sponges
44. couches
45. mailboxes
46. watches
47. toothbrushes
48. wrenches
49. buses
50. nurses
51. patches
52. dishes
53. matches
54. jars
55. bottles
56. handfuls
57. bunches
58. pieces
59. jugs
60. pairs

Lesson 7   page 78

1. men
2. feet
3. women
4. children
5. elves
6. mice
7. fish
8. bookshelves
9. deer
10. calves
11. wolves
12. hooves
13. teeth
14. geese
15. lives
16. sheep
17. soap
18. fruit
19. leaves
20. moose

Lesson 8   page 79

1. teeth
2. calves
3. men
4. scarves
5. knives
6. thieves
7. leaves
8. feet
9. wives
10. halves
11. loaves
12. geese
13. women
14. mice
15. children

16. deer
17. sheep
18. oxen
19. fish
20. shelves

Lesson 9   pages 80-81

1. are
2. am
3. were
4. is
5. was
6. was
7. has
8. were
9. were
10. are
11. were
12. Are
13. is
14. has
15. Were
16. were
17. Are
18. Has
19. have
20. Have
21. Was
22. were
23. Have
24. has
25. Are
26. Is
27. Was
28. dives
29. walks
30. wave
31. fly
32. floats
33. bites
34. drives
35. hop
36. paddles
37. kicks
38. digs
39. sleep
40. ties
41. cut
42. zips
43. writes
44. comb
45. buckles
46. likes
47. cries
48. read
49. sit
50. hangs
51. carries
52. run
53. sweeps
54. swim
55. uses
56. checks
57. weigh
58. eats
59. sees
60. talk
61. stack
62. pour
63. drink
64. hugs
65. go

66. knock
67. rolls
68. treat
69. yells
70. takes
71. are
72. deserve
73. balances

Lesson 10   pages 82-84

1. brushed
2. tied
3. combed
4. jumped
5. buttoned
6. crawled
7. mailed
8. walked
9. hopped
10. colored
11. listened
12. mowed
13. taped
14. raked
15. played
16. zipped
17. rolled
18. locked
19. peeled
20. poured
21. painted
22. bounced
23. called
24. smiled
25. laughed
26. worked
27. galloped
28. raced
29. jogged
30. waited
31. missed
32. lived
33. cared
34. licked
35. finished
36. parted
37. received
38. teased
39. picked
40. chopped
41. moved
42. practiced

Lesson 11   pages 85-87

1. drank
2. fell
3. ate
4. forgot
5. did
6. blew
7. brought
8. went
9. ran
10. built
11. caught
12. chose
13. dug
14. wrote
15. found
16. gave
17. saw
18. threw
19. sat
20. flew
21. wore
22. sold
23. swam
24. thought
25. froze
26. knew
27. left
28. swept
29. met
30. was
31. won
32. bought
33. hid
34. rode
35. took
36. lost
37. taught
38. grew
39. sang
40. shredded
41. hung
42. kept
43. told
44. got
45. held
46. rose
47. made
48. drew
49. bit
50. felt
51. slept
52. sank
53. dove
54. shook

Concepts

Lesson 1   pages 89-90

1. kitchen
2. bedroom
3. classroom
4. freezer
5. grocery store
6. laundry room, laundromat
7. women's or girls' closets or stores
8. men's or boys' closets or stores
9. restaurant
10. zoo
11. farm
12. school
13. movie theater
14. school cafeteria
15. mall
16. fire engine
17. circus
18. parade
19. preschool, kindergarten
20. airplane, jet
21. post office
22. swimming pool
23. beach
24. dentist's office
25. bowling alley
26. beauty shop
27. hospital
28. carnival
29. boat
30. football stadium
31. gas station
32. desert
33. city
34. car
35. ocean
36. forest
37. highway
38. convenience store
39. bank
40. jewelry store

Lesson 2   pages 91-92

1. on
2. in
3. in
4. outside
5. on
6. in
7. at
8. in
9. beside
10. in
11. on
12. on
13. in
14. through
15. at
16. front
17. after
18. out of
19. next to
20. in
21. on
22. out
23. on
24. across
25. on the side
26. down
27. down
28. to
29. away from
30. through
31. close to
32. through
33. away from
34. inside
35. over
36. together
37. bottom
38. in front of
39. across
40. down

Lesson 3   pages 93-94

1. slice an apple
2. light a candle
3. chop wood
4. take pictures
5. make a snowman
6. staple paper together
7. jump out of an airplane
8. slide down hill
9. clean your teeth
10. go to sleep
11. wash a car
12. wrap a present
13. make a sandwich
14. wash your hair
15. wash the dishes
16. make an art project
17. do schoolwork, homework
18. play baseball
19. do yard work
20. eat a meal
21. paint a wall
22. make a salad
23. change baby's diaper
24. take a trip
25. make cookies
26. have a cookout
27. play a board game
28. play tennis
29. wash the floor
30. vacuum the carpet
31. have a party
32. carve a jack o' lantern
33. put up a bulletin board
34. camp out
35. go fishing
36. ride a horse
37. make spaghetti
38. make a tree swing
39. put on a play
40. make something out of wood

Lesson 4   pages 95-96

1. soft, young
2. shiny, hard
3. warm, soft
4. sharp
5. big, tall
6. smelly
7. big, gray
8. light
9. sweet, sticky
10. colorful, pointed
11. cold
12. bright, hot
13. long
14. scary, bumpy
15. fluffy, salty
16. curly, wavy, long
17. wild
18. rough, sharp
19. loud
20. helpful
21. dark
22. mushy, ripe
23. shiny
24. dirty
25. dusty, round
26. funny, lively
27. slippery
28. smooth, long
29. hard, pretty
30. quick
31. sweet, round, juicy
32. smooth, wrinkled, soft
33. salty, crunchy, tasty
34. enormous
35. pretty, fragrant
36. graceful
37. delicious
38. sturdy, useful
39. interesting, exciting
40. breakable, transparent

Lesson 5   page 97

1. soft, furry, toy
2. you color with it, comes in all colors, comes in a box
3. grows, smells good, has leaves and petals

ANSWER KEY

4. has a ladder, is fun, found at playgrounds
5. soft, white, sweet
6. in the bathroom, fill with water, has a drain
7. cleans your teeth, use with toothpaste, prevents cavities
8. has on/off switch, you watch it, can change channel
9. has feathers, is a bird, eaten at Thanksgiving
10. large animal, grey and wrinkled, has a trunk
11. black and white, has stripes, looks like a horse
12. is green, croaks, lives in a pond, eats flies
13. worn on feet, comes in pairs, different styles
14. has long sleeves, covers top part of body, wear in cool weather
15. is red and shiny, has a siren, firemen ride on them
16. soft and fluffy, used on beds, you put your head on it
17. has frosting and candles, tastes sweet, served at a party
18. has horses, goes around, is a fun ride
19. red, yellow or green, fruit, round, grows on trees
20. goes back and forth, sit on it and rock, fun to sit in
21. has a string, goes up and down, can do tricks with it
22. beat on it, is loud, is a musical instrument
23. used to fix hair, has teeth, different sizes
24. is printed with ink, has different sections, can be recycled
25. used to climb to high places, has steps, made of wood or metal
26. wakes us up, has a loud ring, can be set for certain time
27. has black and white keys, is a musical instrument, people sit on a bench to play it
28. used to cut things, is sharp, has handles
29. has straight edge, has numbers on it, used to measure
30. used in the rain, has a handle, comes in many colors
31. used for camping, people sleep in them, has zippers
32. worn on feet, used at skating rinks, can be rented
33. found in kitchen, used to cook, gets hot
34. dries hair, is electric, used in bathroom
35. worn on face, has frame and lenses, help us see

36. found on farms, can be red, animals live there
37. lists names alphabetically, has addresses and phone numbers, has some yellow pages
38. made of metal, used to unlock things, starts car
39. lists months and days, need new one every year, some have pictures
40. used to tell what words mean, used to check spellings, words in alphabetical order

Lesson 6   pages 98-99
1. yes
2. no
3. yes
4. no
5. no
6. yes
7. yes
8. no
9. no
10. yes
11. yes
12. no
13. yes
14. yes
15. no
16. yes
17. yes
18. no
19. yes
20. yes
21. no
22. yes
23. yes
24. no
25. yes
26. yes
27. no
28. no
29. yes
30. yes
31. yes
32. no
33. no
34. no
35. no
36. yes
37. no
38. no
39. yes
40. yes

Lesson 7   pages 100-101
1. before
2. after
3. before
4. last
5. last
6. after
7. afternoon
8. end
9. end
10. before
11. middle
12. beginning
13. before

14. before
15. while it is ringing
16. right now
17. before
18. tomorrow
19. yesterday
20. next month
21. next month
22. now
23. later
24. last part
25. after
26. after
27. during
28. hour
29. one week
30. right now

Lesson 8   pages 102-104
1. tiger
2. chair
3. fire
4. picnic
5. new game
6. water
7. washing your hands
8. pair of shoes
9. apple
10. banana
11. play kick ball
12. mirror
13. multiply numbers
14. day
15. lunch box
16. do your homework
17. sugar
18. lawn mower
19. building a model
20. going swimming
21. dog
22. video game
23. climbing a mountain
24. going to the movies
25. getting a good grade
26. store at noon
27. roller-skating
28. kangaroo
29. riding a bike
30. white shirt

Social Language

Lesson 1   page 106
1. It took me all day. My mom said I had to do it. I hung up all my clothes.
2. I ate pizza at a restaurant. Pepperoni is my favorite kind.
3. I am going to visit my grandparents. They have a swimming pool in their backyard.
4. I went to buy a new pair of shoes. I had to try on six different pairs.
5. I am going to the grocery store with my dad. He lets me pick out my favorite cereal.

6. I was late for school yesterday. It makes me mad when I am late.
7. I played hide-and-seek with my friend Danny. Danny hid behind the couch.
8. I have to give my dog a bath. He got dirty from playing in the mud.
9. I walked home from school in the rain. I felt cold and wet when I got to my house.
10. My aunt and I rode the bus downtown. The bus was big and went fast.
11. I went sliding down a hill in the snow. I went fast and it was fun.
12. I like to go on picnics in the summer. We bring sandwiches and apples.
13. Last summer I watched a parade go by. I saw a big firetruck and a bunch of clowns.
14. I helped my dad rake the leaves and then I jumped in them. We made the pile really big so it was very soft.
15. My class is going on a field trip to the zoo. I want to see the monkeys and tigers.
16. I checked out a book from the library. I read the whole book in three days.
17. I went to get a haircut. The hairdresser cut my hair very short.
18. I went on a trip with my family. We rode in the car all day.
19. I won an award for the art project I made in art class. I painted a painting of a dragon and a castle.
20. My brother and I built a play fort in the backyard. We made it out of old sheets and sticks.
21. Yesterday my tooth fell out. It fell out when I was eating corn on the cob.
22. I fell off the swing and skinned my knee. I went to the school nurse to get a Band-Aid.
23. At Lisa's party we played pin the tail on the donkey. I put my pin by the donkey's nose.
24. Louis likes to pretend he is a superhero. He likes to wear the Superman cape his mom made for him.
25. Last night I spent the night away from home for the first time. At first I felt scared, but my friend made me feel better.
26. Once I got lost in the mall. I went into the toy store by myself and lost my mom and dad.

27. Sometimes at night I think there is a monster underneath my bed. So, I turn on the light to make sure nothing is there.
28. My uncle is teaching me to learn how to ride a bike. I can only ride down the driveway by myself.
29. Yesterday was very windy, so I went to the park with my kite. My kite flew high up in the sky.
30. In art class we learned how to make a bowl out of clay. I was proud of myself when I finished my bowl.
31. I babysat for the neighbor's baby. I liked taking care of the baby.
32. I went to Kara's slumber party. We listened to music, ate pizza, and stayed up very late.
33. I played miniature golf with my friends. It was fun to see who was the best at miniature golf.
34. I have a part in the school play. I get to dress up in a costume and learn lines for the play.
35. I went on the Ferris wheel and got stuck at the top. I was scared until it started moving down again.

Lesson 2   pages 107-108

1. a
2. b
3. b
4. a
5. a
6. b
7. a
8. b
9. a
10. b
11. a
12. a
13. b
14. b
15. b
16. a
17. b
18. b
19. a
20. a
21. b
22. b
23. a
24. b
25. b
26. a
27. b

Lesson 3   pages 109-110

1. Where did you used to live?
2. Hi! Happy Birthday! How are you?
3. When did you get back?

4. I'm surprised to see you home.
5. Have you been waiting long?
6. Do you mind if I play too?
7. Wait...you dropped your ticket.
8. May I borrow your red crayon?
9. What kind of dog is that?
10. What happened to you?
11. What's the matter?
12. No, you don't eat rocks!
13. Where can I find a book on frogs?
14. Did you hurt yourself?
15. What's in the package?
16. Hi, how are you doing?
17. Did you just move here?
18. Are you looking for something?
19. You are skating in the wrong direction.
20. I'll miss you this summer.
21. When is it?
22. Where did you get your sweater?
23. I like your new car.
24. What's wrong? Did you have a bad dream?
25. Excuse me...your lights are still on.
26. That's quite a tie!
27. Is something wrong?
28. Have you been sick?
29. Are you going to paint something?
30. How much is a double scoop?
31. May I please have a balloon?
32. Wait! You drove past our stop.
33. Watch out! Your shoe is untied.
34. This is delicious! Thanks, Mom!
35. I'd like a hamburger and fries, please.
36. I'm sorry I ripped your book.
37. Wow! Those are nice skates!
38. May I please speak to Mrs. Scott?
39. I'm sorry your team lost. You played a good game.
40. I think it's 9 to 7.

Lesson 4   pages 111-112

Accept reasonable answers.

Lesson 5   pages 113-114

Accept reasonable answers.

Lesson 6   page 115

1. There's no snow in the summer.
2. It would't fit.
3. There are no tracks.
4. There would be nobody to find me.
5. It wouldn't get the tangles out.
6. It wouldn't fit through the door.
7. It wouldn't fit in your mouth.
8. I'm too big to fit.

9. The wood is too hard and the scissors wouldn't go through it.
10. A bike without wheels cannot move.
11. You need a racket to hit the ball.
12. It's too small and the rope would get tangled in the hangers and clothes.
13. When you hit it, it would break.
14. Ice cream is made by freezing the ingredients, not heating them.
15. A ruler measures inches not pounds.
16. A rabbit can't bark to tell you when something is wrong.
17. It would be too cold and it might die.
18. The pond wouldn't be frozen in hot weather.
19. If you used oranges, it would be orange juice.
20. If you don't use apples, it won't be apple pie.
21. The driver won't let you on without paying.
22. The water would leak through the material.
23. Since your shoes go on over your socks, you have to take them off first.
24. A bowling ball is too heavy to bounce on the table.
25. You can't see through a refrigerator door.
26. It would get soggy and fall apart.
27. You wouldn't be able to hold them up.
28. Blue and orange don't make green when mixed together.
29. Gasoline will make the fire burn hotter.
30. If you don't open your mouth, you are humming.
31. Elevators are powered by electricity.
32. If you don't bend your knees, you can't get to the next step.
33. The players wouldn't know which checkers were theirs.
34. Once peanuts are ground up, they can't be put back together.
35. There will be a penny left over.
36. The date of your birth doesn't change and your birth certificate can't be changed to a different date.

Lesson 7   page 116

1. He might hurt himself.
2. They might get torn or dirty.
3. Someone might run over it.
4. The soap will get in your eyes and burn them.

5. You won't be able to see traffic.
6. Boots will be heavy and make it hard to swim.
7. The batteries will die.
8. It won't be delivered.
9. The paint will dry and the brush will be ruined.
10. You might trip and fall.
11. You might catch a cold from her.
12. If you spill it, it will stain.
13. The sand will be wet and muddy.
14. You might step on something and hurt your foot.
15. You will burn yourself.
16. It's not polite. You might scare them.
17. You will bother the other people.
18. If you put something heavy on them, they will they will crack.
19. It will ruin your pen and may break the sharpener.
20. If you get in trouble, no one will be there to help you.
21. She might be asleep.
22. The water will get in the wiring and ruin it.
23. It might be too cold for the plants to grow.
24. The food might get on the new clothes and stain them.
25. They might cause blisters on your feet.
26. You won't be able to pay for it and the delivery person will be angry.
27. It will melt.
28. They are supposed to be mixed up to play fair.
29. You might burn your tongue.
30. It will get too hot and the dog could get sick and die.
31. That will make the flames get higher.
32. You don't own it and if you give it away you won't get it back to the library on time.
33. He won't be able to concentrate.
34. The spikes on the bottom will ruin the wood floor.
35. You won't be able to see cars coming up behind you.

Lesson 8   page 117

1. Terriers have short ears.
2. Small cars have two doors.
3. A doll's hair is not real and can't grow.
4. Sometimes I fight with my brother/sister.
5. Leaves fall off trees in autumn.
6. Tigers are too ferocious to make good pets.
7. Some children turn seven in first grade.

8. I learned to walk when I was one.
9. If it has legs, it isn't a snake.
10. If you put water in the freezer, it becomes ice.
11. Lemons are a yellow fruit.
12. You just need to wash it with some soap then you don't have to throw it away.
13. My uncle doesn't have a middle name.
14. Raw carrots are good for you.
15. One of our teachers is a man.
16. This year my birthday was on Monday.
17. There are 12 boys and 13 girls in our class.
18. Moose have antlers.
19. Stan is the tallest in our grade and I'm older than he is.
20. In leap year, it has 29 days.

Defining and Describing

Lesson 1   pages 119-120

1. sitting on
2. drinking
3. sliding down
4. jumping
5. writing
6. cutting
7. calling someone
8. eating
9. hear
10. throwing, kicking, catching
11. taking a bath
12. wash our hair
13. wearing on your feet
14. see
15. playing music
16. rake up leaves
17. make things cold
18. reading
19. blow your nose
20. singing
21. wearing to bed
22. fly
23. cleaning the carpet
24. washing, cleaning
25. hanging up clothes
26. make the bed, sleep on
27. watching a program
28. wearing
29. keep the rain off
30. eating, writing
31. climb
32. dry off
33. making you well, feel better
34. giving, opening
35. riding
36. spending, saving
37. seeing in the dark
38. keeping foods cold
39. climbing
40. get somewhere, put something together

Lesson 2   pages 121-122

1. we go to bed
2. we brush our teeth
3. the teacher teaches
4. we eat breakfast
5. it rings
6. it's morning or night
7. it is cold outside
8. I'm going to school/town
9. we're dirty, it's morning
10. they are tired
11. it's summer, hot
12. we need to tell time
13. pencils are dull or broken
14. we go to school
15. we are thirsty
16. we clean up spills
17. we see a fire
18. we need a book or to look up something
19. we mail a letter
20. we want to ride a bus
21. it is fall
22. it is windy
23. you eat soup, you stir something
24. we are sick
25. we take them off
26. we want to see a movie
27. they watch a movie
28. they are dirty
29. you cut something
30. going to the hospital
31. it is snowing
32. the old one burns out
33. we hook papers together
34. watching a video, recording a show
35. plowing a field
36. you play tennis, racquetball or badminton
37. you're in a boat
38. we take lessons
39. paying bills, at the grocery store
40. the car is broken

Lesson 3   pages 123-125

1. cold
2. round, colorful
3. sticky
4. long, skinny
5. soft, light
6. hard
7. good, like bread
8. smooth, hard
9. round, small
10. big, gray
11. cold, creamy
12. light
13. hot
14. sad
15. salty
16. cold
17. scary
18. rough, hard
19. big
20. pretty, colorful
21. hot
22. sweet
23. loud, shiny
24. rough, prickly
25. flat, round
26. green
27. cold, good
28. rough, soft, prickly
29. sweet, pretty
30. clean, dirty, shiny
31. smelly, black and white
32. loud, scary
33. sweet
34. wet, rough
35. sour, delicious
36. quiet
37. silly, funny
38. small, hard, salty
39. loud
40. rough
41. loud
42. sweet, sour
43. wet, gooey, dirty
44. soft, light
45. rough
46. soft, beautiful
47. smooth, soft
48. rotten, awful
49. hard, cold
50. nice, old, young
51. skinny, long
52. tall
53. scary
54. dusty, clean
55. clear, beautiful
56. dark, fluffy, pretty
57. wrinkled, small
58. soft, sweet, little
59. sweet, strong, good
60. heavy, warm

Lesson 4   pages 126-127

1. animals
2. drink
3. dessert, dairy product
4. color
5. fruit
6. body part
7. clothing
8. vegetables
9. day, part of a weekend
10. farm animals
11. fruit
12. bird
13. snack, treat
14. transportation item
15. drink
16. instrument
17. insects, bugs
18. furniture
19. sport, game
20. farm animals
21. clothing
22. body part
23. shape
24. flowers
25. family member
26. vegetable
27. jewelry
28. toys
29. meat
30. wild/zoo animal
31. musical instrument
32. furniture
33. animal
34. weather
35. illness
36. seasons
37. tool
38. emergency vehicle
39. utensil
40. appliance

Lesson 5   pages 128-129

1. flies
2. cooks
3. plays, imagines
4. writes
5. teach, write, correct
6. colors
7. cleans
8. chew
9. roll
10. cut, snip
11. zips
12. listen
13. buckles
14. tie
15. fall, blow
16. sticks
17. smell
18. cut, mow
19. flies
20. barks, growls, bites
21. melts, falls
22. shut, open, lock
23. crawls
24. dives
25. digs
26. runs, gallops, trots
27. shoots
28. swim
29. pulls, plows
30. rings
31. pops
32. bakes
33. cluck, lay
34. spins
35. blooms, grows
36. pounds, hits
37. falls
38. melts, chills
39. grow
40. quack, waddle
41. burns
42. sees, blinks, winks
43. blows
44. cover
45. tells time, ticks
46. hits, swings
47. open, shut, break, lock
48. holds
49. covers
50. sings, chirps
51. hop
52. beat, pump, break
53. chop
54. stir, mix
55. corrects, erases
56. listens, learns, studies
57. hurts, heals
58. crack, cook
59. cools, blows
60. examines, treats, prescribes
61. covers, disguises, hides
62. shines
63. toast
64. tapes, plays, records
65. blend, mix
66. add, subtract, compute
67. deliver
68. measure

ANSWER KEY

69. boils, freezes, runs, flows, leaks
70. crows
71. travel, sightsee
72. sinks, holds
73. paint, draw, create
74. floats
75. stretches, holds
76. sweetens
77. reflect
78. cover
79. sticks
80. paddles

Lesson 6   pages 130-131

1. soft, furry, black, little
2. new/old, dirty/clean
3. short/tall, green
4. square, wooden, color
5. round, delicious, fruit/cream
6. colors, fat/skinny, broken, new
7. new/old, big/little, warm, colorful
8. cold/warm, fresh/spoiled, chocolate/skim
9. sticky, sweet, crunchy/smooth
10. round, plastic/ceramic/glass, dirty/clean
11. pretty, colorful, dead/alive, short/tall
12. sharp/dull, plastic/metal, big/little, short/tall
13. cold, melted, flavors, big/little, good/tasty
14. thick/thin, fresh/stale, big/little, type, tasty
15. tube/bottle, color, full/empty, taste
16. thick/thin, old/new, big/little
17. big/little, color, dirty/clean, soft, lady's, man's
18. big/little, type, fancy/simple, slow/fast
19. little, red/black, tiny, light
20. big/little, play/real, old/new, loud, color
21. color, small, furry, smelly
22. old/new, soft/itchy, color, boys/girls, design
23. big/little, old/new, color/black-white
24. green, short/long, dry/wet
25. yellow, long/short, big
26. rectangular/square, old/new, shiny
27. round, fuzzy, color, light, new/old
28. flavor, type of cone, big/little, melted
29. long/short, wooden/plastic, heavy/light, color
30. white, hard, shell, yellow center
31. red, ripe, sweet, hard/mushy, big/little
32. old, hair color
33. brown/white, small, amount of, wet/dry
34. white, fresh/stale, hot, buttered/salted, fluffy
35. big, baby/adult, furry, ferocious, wild, color

36. size, new/old, color, fast
37. tall/short, new/old, pretty/ugly
38. plump/skinny, beef/chicken/turkey, cooked/raw
39. big/little, sharp/dull, wooden/plastic, long/short
40. shape, color/design, big/little, new/old
41. new/old, band type/width/material, digital/clock face, gold/silver/color
42. length, color, new/old, thick/thin
43. colors, long/short, thin/thick, plastic
44. big/little, ripe, sweet, color, shape
45. colors, long/short, thin/thick, plastic
46. big/little, cold, tall/short, fat/skinny
47. long/short, cooked, tasty, thin, color
48. metal/wooden, long/short, tall/short, new/old
49. hot, wood, smoky
50. sunny, hot, sandy, salty, windy
51. sweet, white/brown, light
52. shape, sticky, color, amount, old/new
53. type, old/new, color, ink color, length
54. tall/short, wide/narrow, clean/dirty, wooden/metal, type, big/little
55. small/large, color, young/old, fresh/frozen, cooked, fried, raw, spoiled
56. color, fragrant, liquid
57. tall/short, fragrant, color, fat/skinny, smooth/rough, new/old
58. tall/short, shape, locked/unlocked, wooden/metal
59. smelly, slick/slimy, smooth/rough, color, big/little
60. soft/hard, wooden/metal/brass, size, made/unmade
61. metal, hard, color, old/new
62. long/short, toy/real, type, color
63. soft/hard, color, type, new/old, heavy/light
64. color, furry, wild, scary, big/little, young/old
65. stale/fresh, white/dark/rye, sliced/loaf, thick/thin
66. bright, color, bolts, scary
67. short/long, big/little, color, wool/silk, girls/ladies
68. bright, full/half/crescent, color
69. old/new, thick/thin, black and white, pictures
70. shape, sweet, decorated, chocolate, flavor
71. long/short, wool/silk, warm, colors

72. orange, crunchy, thin/thick, vegetable
73. long/short, gold/silver, color, expensive/cheap, dull/shiny, old/new
74. shape, colors, bright, metal/wooden
75. big/little, old/new, color
76. round, noisy, color, big/little
77. small/big, square, weighs
78. open/closed, full/self-serve, clean/dirty, busy, expensive
79. sharp, small/large, long/short
80. deep/shallow, type, wide/narrow, muddy/dry

Lesson 7   page 132

1. you can color with them, you can hold both in your hand
2. both are worn, keep you warm
3. both cut, are sharp, have handles
4. both take you places, charge you money, have wheels
5. both are worn, tied around the neck
6. both are body parts, bend
7. both are used to blow your nose, are soft
8. both are read, have covers and pages
9. both tell time
10. both are worn on the hands, keep hands warm
11. both are used to clean the body
12. both are animals, have 4 legs
13. both can make music, played by blowing
14. both are worn on the feet
15. both are hair on the face
16. both can be sat on, can hold more than one person
17. both are baby animals
18. both are male relatives
19. both are round, red, can be eaten
20. both go up, have steps, are climbed
21. both are light and soft
22. both can be popped, both are filled with air
23. both are sharp, hold things together
24. both are used to pack things, are carried
25. both are for cars
26. both are worn at night
27. both are sharp
28. both are used in the water, float, carry people
29. both are musical instruments, have strings
30. both can be ridden, have handlebars, have two wheels
31. both are bodies of water
32. both are lived in
33. both provide information, are alphabetical
34. both are used to fasten clothing

35. both record, use tape, have microphones
36. both are used to cut, are sharp, are metal
37. both are seen at night, in the sky, bright, far away
38. both help you see better
39. both are put on the body, make you smell better
40. both have lenses, are used to see things far away

Lesson 8   page 133

1. a truck goes on land, a boat goes on water
2. you smell with your nose and hear with your ear
3. a sister is a girl, a brother is a boy
4. a vacuum sucks up dirt and a broom sweeps it up
5. an elephant is big, a fox is little; an elephant has skin, a fox has fur
6. a drum is beaten, a guitar is strummed; the guitar has strings, a drum doesn't
7. a watermelon is big, an apple is small
8. you hug with your arms, you kiss with your lips
9. a marble is small, a bowling ball is big; a marble is light, a bowling ball is heavy
10. ketchup is red and mustard is yellow
11. a ring is on your finger and a bracelet is on your wrist or arm
12. a washcloth is smaller than a towel; a washcloth is to wash with and a towel is to dry off with
13. roller skates have wheels, ice skates have blades; ice skates are used on ice
14. gloves have a place for each finger separately
15. milk comes from cows, juice from fruit; milk is white, juice colored
16. snow is frozen water, rain is not; snow is white, rain is clear
17. a train goes on a track, a car goes on a road; a train has many cars, a car is only one
18. tiger has black stripes, lion has no stripes; lion has a mane, tiger doesn't
19. tree is big, rose is little; tree has bark, rose has thorns
20. suitcase is larger than a purse; suitcases are for clothes, purse is not
21. hammer is used to hit, saw is used to cut; saw is sharp, hammer isn't
22. sunglasses have dark lenses, eyeglasses have clear lenses
23. lime is green, lemon is yellow

ANSWER KEY

24. beach has sand, mountaintop has dirt, beach is low altitude, mountaintop is high
25. sun is hot, moon is not; moon is bright at night, sun is bright in the day
26. zipper is long and narrow with teeth, buttons are usually round
27. square has four sides, triangle has three
28. light bulb uses electricity, candle does not
29. a laugh is when you are happy, cry is when you are sad
30. a bird is a living thing, an airplane is a machine
31. a sneeze comes from your nose, a cough from you mouth, chest, throat
32. doctor helps sick people, fire fighter puts out fires
33. library has book, grocery store has groceries
34. shampoo is for hair, toothpaste is for teeth
35. pizza has a crust, spaghetti doesn't
36. carrot is orange, potato is white/brownish
37. basement is at the bottom, attic is at the top
38. kite is flat, balloon is blown up round
39. string is thin, rope is thick
40. a waterfall is outside, a shower is in bathroom; a waterfall comes from rivers, a rain shower comes from the sky

Written Language

Lesson 1   pages 135-137
1. ball
2. car
3. bee
4. knife
5. tree
6. lamp
7. key
8. banana
9. doctor
10. book
11. bus
12. bat
13. cup
14. coat
15. hat
16. rain
17. clock
18. nose
19. bird
20. boots
21. flag
22. elephant
23. stamp, sticker
24. clown

Lesson 2   pages 138-139
1. car, truck
2. picture
3. gloves, mittens
4. drink, glass of water
5. television
6. water
7. bed
8. hamburger, hot dog
9. telephone
10. school bus
11. ball
12. grocery store
13. wrist, arm
14. butter, jelly
15. doctor, dentist
16. rings
17. chalkboard, blackboard
18. popcorn, candy
19. baths
20. sky
21. belt
22. toothbrush, toothpaste
23. tissue, handkerchief
24. wallet, purse, bank
25. stove
26. scissors, clippers
27. thunder
28. helmet
29. newspaper
30. alarm, mom, dad
31. match
32. suitcase, bag
33. camera
34. kite
35. candles
36. tree
37. stamp
38. lunchroom, cafeteria
39. thank you
40. moon, stars

Lesson 3   pages 140-141
1. dish; dog food; pour; water
2. clothes; breakfast; teeth; hair
3. book; desk/counter; card; Thank
4. pencil/pen; book; Read; paper
5. telephone book; telephone; number; friend
6. water; shampoo; hair; towel
7. paper; box/present; tape; bow
8. paper, stationary; pen/pencil; address; envelope
9. trash/garbage; trash; close/tie; outside
10. lawnmower; gas; engine; yard/grass

Lesson 4   pages 142-144
1. Dan loves scrambled eggs.
2. I see a big dog.
3. Karl climbs a tall tree.
4. Jane draws a pretty picture.
5. Bonnie eats vanilla ice cream.
6. Gail reads the big, long, scary book.
7. Jay blew up the red, big balloon.
8. Matt sweeps the dirty, dusty floor.
9. Ivan broke the full, new glass.
10. Ben steps in a big, deep, muddy hole.
11. Laura sleeps in her big, new bed.
12. George pulls the red, little wagon.
13. Melanie tasted the sour lemon.
14. The teacher shut the heavy, big, back door.
15. James helped the old, young, sad, happy woman.
16. Juan's new, brown shoes were too big.
17. The large, tall, heavy bookshelves in Dave's room are full.
18. They went into the dark, big, empty room.
19. Brian combs his long, short, wet, messy hair.
20. Oscar touched the cold, hard, brown, big, little rock.
21. The old, broken toy wouldn't work.
22. My friends skate on the frozen lake.
23. The cold drink was refreshing.
24. We laughed at the funny movie.
25. You must be very quiet in the library.
26. The man snored loudly, softly in his sleep.
27. The rabbits hop quickly, quietly through the bushes.
28. Tom saw the shiny, bright star in the sky.
29. The burned toast was black.
30. Turtles crawl slowly over the rock.

Lesson 5   pages 145-147
1. She ate cereal for breakfast.
2. She got ready for bed.
3. He was going to take a picture.
4. She was getting ready to go out in the rain.
5. He was going to school.
6. They had a birthday party.
7. Mrs. James went to the park.
8. He saw a fire engine.
9. She flew a kite.
10. She was going swimming.
11. We went to the zoo.
12. They went on a picnic.
13. He was going on a bike trip.
14. He played a basketball game in the gym.
15. They went to the farm.
16. She went to the grocery store.
17. He was going to tape a program or movie.
18. They can be found in outer space.

Lesson 6   pages 148-150
1. cereal
   drink
   bowl
   eat
   milk
2. play
   slide
   climb
   run
   friend
3. piano, drum, trumpet
   plays
   drums
   blow
   class, music
   band
4. white, heavy
   school
   boots
   gloves, mittens
   snowman, fort
   threw
   wet, cold, tired
   hot
5. newspaper
   reads, looks at
   eats
   page
   newspaper
   very
6. party
   years
   delicious, pretty, big
   candles
   bright, hot, pretty
   cut
   chocolate, strawberry
   hard, cold, delicious, good
   bake
   birthday
7. pet
   little
   feed
   walk
   dog
   puppies
   biggest
8. terrible, scary
   house
   dark
   hear
   scared
   to, toward
   light
   bed, house, bedroom
9. bad, nasty, horrible
   tissues
   doctor
   medicine
   much, a lot
   blow, wipe
10. trip
   pack, bring
   bus, car
   big
   skinny
   wore
   cool, windy
   around
   sat
   ate
   soon

Lesson 7 pages 151-153

1. 1,3,2
2. 2,3,1
3. 2,1,3
4. 3,1,2
5. 2,3,1
6. 3,2,1
7. 1,3,2
8. 2,1,3
9. 2,1,3
10. 2,3,1
11. 4,2,3,1
12. 1,3,4,2
13. 2,3,4,1
14. 3,4,2,1

Processing Information

Lesson 1 pages 155-156

1. 2,1,3
2. 3,1,2
3. 2,1,3
4. 3,1,2
5. 3,1,2
6. 2,1,3
7. 1,3,2
8. 3,2,1
9. 3,2,1
10. 1,2,3
11. 3,2,1
12. 4,2,3,1
13. 2,1,4,3
14. 2,3,4,1
15. 3,1,2,4
16. 3,4,1,2
17. 3,1,2,4
18. 4,1,3,2

Lesson 2 pages 157-159

1. 1,2,3
2. 1,2,3
3. 3,2,1
4. 3,1,2
5. 3,2,1
6. 1,3,2
7. 3,2,1
8. 3,2,1
9. 1,3,2
10. 1,3,2
11. 3,1,2
12. 1,2,3
13. 3,2,1
14. 3,2,1
15. 3,1,2
16. 3,1,2
17. 1,2,3
18. 1,3,2
19. 3,2,1
20. 1,3,2
21. 2,1,3
22. 1,2,3
23. 4,3,1,2
24. 1,2,4,3
25. 2,4,3,1
26. 4,3,1,2
27. 4,1,2,3

Lesson 3 pages 160-161
Answers will vary.

Lesson 4 pages 162-167

Toy Store
1. three
2. toy soldier
3. books
4. boy
5. two balls
6. lion
7. wagon
8. football
9. kite and airplane
10. kite

Barnyard
1. henhouse
2. duck
3. crow, bird
4. cat
5. rooster
6. dog
7. barn and fence
8. sheep, mouse, chickens
9. eight
10. chickens

Classroom
1. the teacher's
2. chalkboard
3. clock, calendar
4. aquarium
5. two
6. two
7. three
8. calendar
9. map
10. plants

Kitchen
1. a cat
2. child's drawing, picture
3. bowl of fruit
4. cat on rug
5. window
6. loaf of bread
7. pair of scissors
8. knife
9. scissors, clock
10. dishwasher, loaf of bread

Playground
1. merry-go-round
2. see-saw
3. slide
4. jungle gym, swings
5. swings
6. see-saw
7. jungle gym, slide, bench
8. see-saw, swings
9. jungle gym, slide, bench
10. merry-go-round

Campground
1. boys'
2. girls'
3. girls'
4. boys'
5. boys'
6. bridge
7. beach
8. camp entrance
9. bridge, lake
10. dining hall

Lesson 5 pages 168-169

1. My favorite color is red.
2. My shirt is wet.
3. Squirrels like nuts.
4. Knives are sharp.
5. My bike has a flat tire.
6. Pickles are sour.
7. Yesterday it snowed.
8. The pie is hot.
9. The lawn mower is noisy.
10. My dog likes to eat ice cream.
11. I hit my finger with a hammer.
12. Our neighbor drives a truck.
13. The clothes in the dryer are still wet.
14. My father works for the city.
15. I'm going to wear my blue dress to the party.
16. My uncle lives in California.
17. My dad and I went for a walk in the woods.
18. Bears can be dangerous.
19. Memorial Day is in May.
20. Too much salt will ruin the soup.
21. Bacon tastes good with pancakes.
22. Be careful when you use a hair dryer.
23. Why don't you look for the bus?
24. Joe's brother is a hockey star.
25. My dad likes to play the piano.
26. Our room number is 17.
27. Don't put your comb on the kitchen table.
28. The math assignment begins on page five.
29. Blue jays are noisy.
30. A tool for carving wood is called a chisel.

Lesson 6 pages 170-172

1. a
2. b
3. a
4. a
5. a
6. b
7. b
8. b
9. a
10. a
11. b
12. a
13. a
14. b
15. b
16. a
17. a
18. a

Lesson 7 pages 173-174

1. Feed the dog — don't forget!
2. Watch show at 8:00 on Friday.
3. Bring sleeping bag to party.
4. Dad's birthday is on Monday.
5. Bring library books to school tomorrow.
6. Dad, buy more bread.
7. Mom—Dora called.
8. Grandmother invited us to dinner on Sunday.
9. Buy Grandpa wrenches for his birthday.
10. Be at school by 7:30 on Friday.
11. Mom—I'm at Deana's.
12. Do pages 5 and 6 for math.
13. Library hours—until 9:00 Monday and Wednesday.
14. Dad—your car can be picked up after 5:00.
15. Movie starts at 1:15, 4:00, and 7:30.
16. 2 batteries, notebook paper, birthday present
17. one large pepperoni with extra cheese, one small plain

Self-Expression

Lesson 1 pages 176-178

1. soap, water
2. books, bus
3. toothpaste, toothbrush
4. cereal, spoon
5. markers, crayons
6. soap, sink
7. paper, pencil, book
8. hoop, ball
9. collar, leash
10. umbrella, raincoat
11. helmet, handlebars
12. stamp, envelope
13. sheets, quilt
14. number, phone
15. forks, napkins
16. bread, peanut butter
17. matches, wood
18. camera, film
19. dustpan, broom
20. blanket, coat
21. food, cart
22. scissors, clippers
23. doctor, medicine
24. saddle, reins
25. seeds, dirt, water
26. kernels, oil, salt
27. wand, liquid soap
28. librarian, book, shelves
29. bowl, hot water, spoon
30. theater, actors

Lesson 2 pages 179-181

1. a cup
2. crayons, markers
3. a scissors, clippers
4. a toothbrush, toothpaste
5. a pencil, pen
6. a spoon
7. bread, a toaster
8. a towel
9. a brush, comb
10. a light, lamp, flashlight, candle
11. teeth
12. a phone number
13. a key
14. a knife
15. gloves, mittens, pockets
16. a chair

17. a broom
18. a camera
19. a saw, an axe
20. a rake, leaf blower
21. shampoo, soap
22. glasses, contacts
23. a bus, bicycle, parent's car
24. money
25. medicine, rest, sleep
26. a spoon, cone
27. a boat, raft
28. boots
29. ice
30. a belt
31. a tissue, handkerchief
32. a pole, rod, net, hook
33. a ladder
34. wind, string
35. shoelaces
36. a match
37. water
38. a lawn mower
39. milk, a bottle
40. an umbrella
41. a knife
42. a stamp
43. an alarm clock
44. a sprinkler, hose
45. chalk, a rock
46. a suitcase
47. seeds, water, dirt
48. a scale
49. an eraser
50. a sled
51. a potholder
52. a switch
53. brakes
54. a compass
55. a lid
56. a rubber band, box
57. sticks
58. a net
59. strings, your hand
60. a steering wheel

Lesson 3   pages 182-183

1. no
2. no
3. yes
4. no
5. no
6. yes
7. yes
8. yes
9. yes
10. no
11. yes
12. yes
13. yes
14. yes
15. yes
16. no
17. no
18. yes
19. no
20. yes
21. no
22. no
23. yes
24. yes
25. yes
26. yes
27. no
28. yes
29. yes
30. yes
31. no
32. no
33. no
34. no
35. yes
36. yes
37. no
38. yes
39. yes
40. yes

Lesson 4   pages 184-185

1. c, b, a
2. b, a, c
3. a, b, c
4. c, a, b
5. b, a, c
6. b, c, a
7. c, a, b
8. a, c, b
9. b, c, a
10. b, a, c
11. b, c, a
12. c, b, a
13. c, a, b
14. a, b, c
15. b, c, a
16. b, a, c

Lesson 5   pages 186-187

1. happy
2. scared
3. surprised
4. worried
5. afraid
6. excited
7. hopeful
8. confused
9. nice
10. concerned
11. cheerful
12. sympathetic
13. grumpy
14. proud
15. hurt
16. selfish
17. surprised
18. embarrassed
19. relieved
20. miserable

Lesson 6   pages 188-189

1. lonely
2. angry
3. likes her, thinks she is nice
4. excited, happy
5. proud, happy
6. sorry, sad
7. disappointed, sad
8. grumpy, irritated, angry
9. embarrassed, annoyed, upset
10. worried
11. afraid, frightened
12. thankful, grateful
13. sympathetic, sad
14. merry, happy, cheerful
15. weary, tired, exhausted, fatigued
16. nervous
17. confused
18. lonely, sad
19. guilty
20. frustrated, unhappy

Lesson 7   page 190

1. you will be clean
2. you won't be hungry
3. you can get well
4. you might get burned
5. you won't miss the bus
6. it won't melt
7. you won't trip; your shoes will stay on
8. she won't worry
9. your feet won't get cold or wet
10. they won't die
11. you don't get wet
12. you might get lost
13. it is their birthday; you want to wish them a happy birthday
14. it won't dry up
15. you can learn to spell; you can get them all right on your test
16. you won't disturb anyone; people can read/think
17. you can remember what you learned
18. it could shock you
19. they could make you sick; they might be poisonous
20. you don't get the floor all wet

Lesson 8   page 191

Answers will vary.

1-4-123567